ALL ABOUT TOWN

Activities for Learning Language

by
Constance F. McCarthy
and
Ann D. Sheehy

Illustrations by Vincenza Genovese

**Communication
Skill Builders**
3830 E. Bellevue/P.O. Box 42050
Tucson, Arizona 85733
(602) 323-7500

914-679-5966

M.E. Alberta

Duplicating

You may prefer to copy the designated reproducible materials by using stencils or spirit masters. It is not necessary to tear pages out of this book. Make a single photocopy of the desired page. Use that photocopy to make a stencil or spirit master on a thermal copier.

© 1987 by

**Communication
Skill Builders, Inc.**
3830 E. Bellevue/P.O. Box 42050
Tucson, Arizona 85733
(602) 323-7500

ISBN 0-88450-250-3   Catalog No. 7437

10 9 8 7 6 5 4 3 2
Printed in the United States of America

About the Authors

Constance F. McCarthy is a speech/language pathologist in a self-contained oral language classroom in Phoenix, Arizona. She received her masters degree in Speech and Language Pathology and Audiology from Syracuse University. Ms. McCarthy holds the Certificate of Clinical Competence from the American Speech-Language-Hearing Association. Coauthor **Ann D. Sheehy** earned her B.S. degree in Speech and Language Pathology and Audiology at Arizona State University. Ms. Sheehy is employed as a speech/language pathologist in the Phoenix public school system.

Contents

Introduction

The materials in *All About Town* provide opportunities for children to acquire and use receptive and expressive language skills while exploring and learning about their environment. Use of the materials as suggested will increase language competency, assist in achieving successful academic performance, and promote acceptable social behavior. The instructional information, which is a recognized part of a kindergarten/first grade curriculum, serves as a vehicle for teaching vocabulary and making language concepts meaningful. In return, the organized language activities provide a framework for teaching the pertinent information of the curriculum. The combination encourages learning how to learn.

Another in the *All About* series, *All About Town* expands on *All About Me*, which helps children develop positive self-images by increasing language competencies and achieving academic success. *All About Town* helps the child extend this positive self-image to the home, the school, and the community. The books can be used separately; the vocabulary, language skills and concepts presented here begin at the level of *All About Me* and gradually become more complex. The tasks reinforce those skills already presented by using them in conjunction with new skills, thereby providing continuity in learning.

Activities for Learning Language

Effective language in a classroom setting is a complicated process. Some children enter school better equipped than others to meet the challenge. Success is largely dependent on the child's pragmatic language abilities: Is the child able to respond positively to a new adult in charge? Does the child interact appropriately with a new group of peers? Can the new student understand and follow a classroom routine, listen for extended periods of time, follow directions, and complete a paper-and-pencil task?

The activities in this volume promote the development of pragmatic language skills. The instructional information they contain, which is required as part of the kindergarten/first grade curriculum, serves as a vehicle for teaching vocabulary and language concepts. The materials were developed in an oral language disorders classroom, where children with severe communication disorders were being prepared for successful performance in regular classrooms. The primary deficits identified in the children were in speech and language, but their communication problems were manifested in many areas including lack of organization in behavior and learning, difficulty in attending to and completing a task, and behaviors indicating poor self-image. The language curriculum was designed to assist them in increasing their language competencies, achieving successful academic performance, and establishing acceptable classroom behavior.

All of the activities have been used successfully in regular and self-contained language-learning disabilities classrooms, and in individual and group speech and language therapy. The children in a regular classroom complete these activities at a faster pace than those with language-learning disabilities, but the information and skills presented are essential to positive performance for both groups.

Materials

The activities in *All About Town* provide many opportunities to help children acquire receptive and expressive language skills necessary for developing a positive self-image. The materials include reproducible worksheets, "let's pretend" activities, art and science projects, and bulletin board patterns. They are organized by topic and may be used in any order, as needed.

The reproducible worksheets are a visual representation of classroom activities. They are designed to help strengthen sequencing ability, develop spatial concepts, and expand vocabulary and classification skills. They provide opportunities for practicing and demonstrating language skills when following directions, explaining answers, and asking questions.

"Let's pretend" activities allow the children to practice oral communication with limited risk. Self-expression is encouraged through the use of puppets and masks. The activities also help the children learn to distinguish between reality and make-believe.

The science projects teach sequencing and cause and effect. They provide natural opportunities for talking about ideas and asking questions, and frequently they stimulate discussions at home when other activities have failed.

The art activities help the children learn to follow directions and develop fine motor skills. When the children take home a completed project to share with family members, they gain a sense of accomplishment and improved self-esteem.

The instructional bulletin boards reinforce vocabulary, spatial concepts, and other general information presented in daily activities. They can be used for demonstration and review. Participating in bulletin board activities gives children a sense of being part of a group.

All About Town presents these components as a complete unit. There is enough repetition for practice and enough variety to maintain the children's interest.

Using the Materials

1. Discuss with the children all the information presented. Give them the opportunity to talk about their ideas, make choices, explain their answers, and ask questions. Let the children talk. The best way to develop oral communication skills is to practice using them in a meaningful learning situation.

2. Check frequently to be sure the children understand what is expected of them. Encourage them to ask clarification questions when necessary.

3. Simple directions are given for each activity, project, or worksheet. Learning to follow directions is an integral part of the program. Successful participation in the activities will help establish a positive self-image through increased understanding of classroom routine, effective experiences in verbal expression, and completion of academic worksheets.

4. Explain to the children that broken lines indicate cutting.

5. The amount of coloring on the worksheets can be varied, according to lesson objectives. If practice on fine motor skills is needed, the pictures should be used as is. If practice in following directions is needed, specific coloring instructions may be used and monitored. Coloring on some pages may be optional and used as an independent activity.

6. Worksheets and projects are designed to be sent home for practice and review of material. They are also an effective means of communicating with parents.

7. Use blank worksheet grids (pages 11-13) to design additional worksheets, using favorite pictures.

8. Many pictures of faces may be used for making masks. Enlarge the faces with an opaque projector, trace them onto paper, color or paint them, and cut them out.

9. The large pictures of faces may be used for making paper-bag puppets. Reproduce the pictures for the children. Instruct them to color and cut out the pictures. Mount the faces on the bottom of a paper bag, being careful not to glue the flap shut. Slide one hand into the bag, bend the four fingers over the fold, and move the fingers to make the puppet's head nod.

10. Small books can be made using many of the pictures. Cut 9″ x 12″ sheets of construction paper in half lengthwise. Decide on the number of pages needed, and distribute strips accordingly. (Two strips become a front cover, back cover, and four pages.) Assemble the books by folding the strips in half and fastening them together along the fold with staples or fasteners. The book will measure 4½″ x 6″.

11. Many of the pictures can be used to make classroom posters. Mount the pictures showing classroom behavior on tagboard and post them to illustrate the rules. Posters can also illustrate buildings, vehicles, careers . . .

Goals and Objectives

The goals and objectives of the program match the activities and are based on 80% mastery. They are suitable as stated for use on an IEP.

Long-term Goals:

To develop receptive and expressive language competencies needed to function in a classroom setting.

To develop a positive self-image through increased understanding of classroom expectations and successful academic performance.

To expand semantic comprehension and usage.

To improve functional use of language.

To improve interpersonal communication skills.

To improve fine motor skills.

Short-term Objectives:

Child will

1. demonstrate understanding of same/different by identification of objects in four out of five trials in a language activity.

2. understand physical attributes and group objects accordingly in four out of five trials in a language activity.

3. understand the concept of classification and sort familiar objects according to property and/or function in four out of five trials in a language activity.

4. identify and name vehicles with 80% accuracy in a language activity.

5. understand the properties of vehicles and classify accordingly in four out of five trials in a language activity.

6. identify and name community places with 80% accuracy in a language activity.

7. understand the properties of community places and classify accordingly in four out of five trials in a language activity.

8. identify persons and their occupations with 80% accuracy in a language activity.

9. understand the persons and their occupations and classify accordingly in four out of five trials in a language activity.

10. identify and name articles of clothing with 80% accuracy in a language activity.

11. understand the properties of clothing and classify accordingly in four out of five trials in a language activity.

12. identify and name food items with 80% accuracy in a language activity.

13. understand the properties of food and classify accordingly in four out of five trials in a language activity.

14. identify and name tools with 80% accuracy in a language activity.

15. understand the properties of tools and classify accordingly in four out of five trials in a language activity.

16. identify and name toys with 80% accuracy in a language activity.

17. understand the properties of toys and classify accordingly in four out of five trials in a language activity.

18. identify and name pets with 80% accuracy in a language activity.

19. understand the properties of pets and classify accordingly in four out of five trials in a language activity.

20. identify and name household items with 80% accuracy in a language activity.

21. understand the properties of household items and classify accordingly in four out of five trials in a language activity.

22. demonstrate understanding of spatial concepts by using precise vocabulary to describe where people or objects are located in four out of five trials.

23. understand and provide the appropriate WH word in accurately produced questions in four out of five trials in a language activity.

24. use precise vocabulary to describe actions in picture stories and/or while relating an event or experience in four out of five trials in a language activity.

25. demonstrate understanding of sequencing by arranging three or four story pictures in correct time order and justifying order.

26. demonstrate understanding of real and pretend in four out of five trials in a language activity.

27. act out or provide dialogue for a role in a story or play.

28. demonstrate awareness of classroom routine by following the rules in 80% of the activities on a given day.

29. participate effectively in a peer discussion group in four out of five trials.

30. process oral directions for paper-and-pencil tasks requiring memory of one critical element in four out of five trials.

31. process oral directions for paper-and-pencil tasks requiring memory of two critical elements in four out of five trials.

32. process oral directions for paper-and-pencil tasks requiring memory of three or more critical elements in four out of five trials.

33. stay within the lines on four out of five objects when coloring a worksheet or other activity.

34. cut on the cutting line of four out of five objects when completing a worksheet or other activity.

Class Record Sheet for Mastery

Write the names in the left-hand column.

Write titles of Worksheets in top columns as they are completed.

Write date or comment in box, or use (+) or (—) for task completion.

Name										
1.										
2.										
3.										
4.										
5.										
6.										
7.										
8.										
9.										
10.										
11.										
12.										
13.										
14.										
15.										
16.										
17.										
18.										
19.										
20.										
21.										
22.										
23.										
24.										
25.										

Class Record Sheet for Mastery (continued)

1.													
2.													
3.													
4.													
5.													
6.													
7.													
8.													
9.													
10.													
11.													
12.													
13.													
14.													
15.													
16.													
17.													
18.													
19.													
20.													
21.													
22.													
23.													
24.													
25.													

Vocabulary Inventory

Name _____

FURNITURE

	Date: _____		Date: _____	
	Receptive	Expressive	Receptive	Expressive
sink				
stove				
refrigerator				
lavatory				
toilet				
bathtub				
table				
chair				
lamp				
bed				
dresser				
rug				
couch (sofa)				
television set				
bookshelf (bookcase)				

TOOLS

	Date: _____		Date: _____	
	Receptive	Expressive	Receptive	Expressive
hammer				
drill				
screwdriver				
pliers				
saw				
wrench				
toolbox				

PEOPLE AT SCHOOL

	Date: _____		Date: _____	
	Receptive	Expressive	Receptive	Expressive
teacher				
principal speech pathologist				
nurse				
custodian				
secretary crossing guard				
librarian cafeteria worker				

COMMUNITY WORKERS

	Date: _____		Date: _____	
	Receptive	Expressive	Receptive	Expressive
mail carrier garbage collector				
police officer business person				
cashier				
doctor				
dentist construction worker				

SIGNS AND SIGNALS

	Date: _____		Date: _____	
	Receptive	Expressive	Receptive	Expressive
stop sign school crossing railroad crossing				
yield				
one way				
telephone				
traffic light				

PARTS OF A HOUSE

	Date: _____		Date: _____	
	Receptive	Expressive	Receptive	Expressive
walls				
roof				
windows				
door				
chimney				
steps				
foundation				

BUILDINGS

	Date: _____		Date: _____	
	Receptive	Expressive	Receptive	Expressive
house				
school				
fire station				
post office				
police station				
fast-food restaurant				
office building				
hotel				
apartment house				
hospital				
bank				
gas station				
shopping center				

VEHICLES

	Date: _____		Date: _____	
	Receptive	Expressive	Receptive	Expressive
station wagon				
car				
van				
jeep				
motorcycle				
pickup truck				
airplane				
front-loader				
sailboat				
helicopter				
police car				
postal jeep				
ambulance				
garbage truck				
school bus				
semitrailer				
fire engine				
train				

CONCEPTS

	Date: _____		Date: _____	
	Receptive	Expressive	Receptive	Expressive
same				
different				
not the same				
belongs				
doesn't belong				
around				
through				
behind				
beside				

OPPOSITES

	Date: _____		Date: _____	
	Receptive	Expressive	Receptive	Expressive
hot/cold				
hard/soft				
wet/dry				
empty/full				
rough/smooth				
real/ make-believe				

CONCEPTS FOR FOLLOWING DIRECTIONS

	Date: _____		Date: _____	
	Receptive	Expressive	Receptive	Expressive
in				
on				
next to				
left				
right				
bottom				
top				
straight				
middle				
first				
another				
more				
big				
small				
under				
corner				
around				

Name _____

Name _____

Name _____

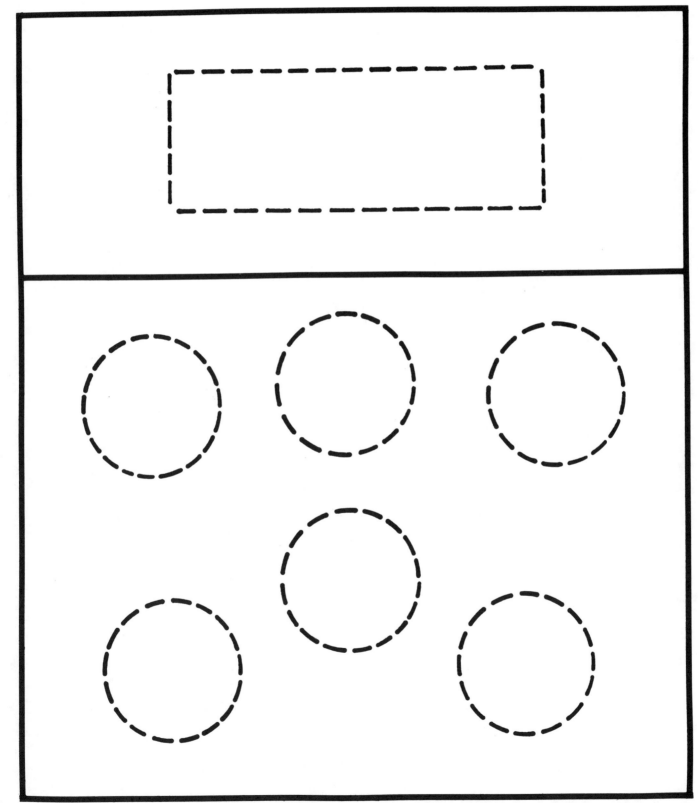

Activities

Family Activities

Talking About the Family

Discuss different kinds of families including those with two parents, a single parent, separated parents, grandparents, and only and multiple children. Have the children tell about their families. Talk about how families are the same and how they are different.

Activities:

1. Make a family portrait:
   Copy and distribute family members to the children. Have the children color and add appropriate details. Encourage the children to make the drawings look like their family members. Glue the figures to a piece of construction paper and add the frame on page 18.

2. Make a diorama using the family figures.

3. Make a school scene, using the pictures of the children with the school picture on page 36.

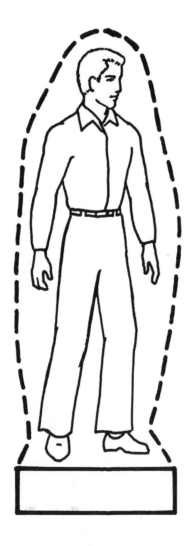

Name _____

Name _____

Family Portrait

Name _____

These People Live at My House

Talk with the children about their families.

Instruct them to draw in each window a person who lives at their house. Have them include a picture of themselves.

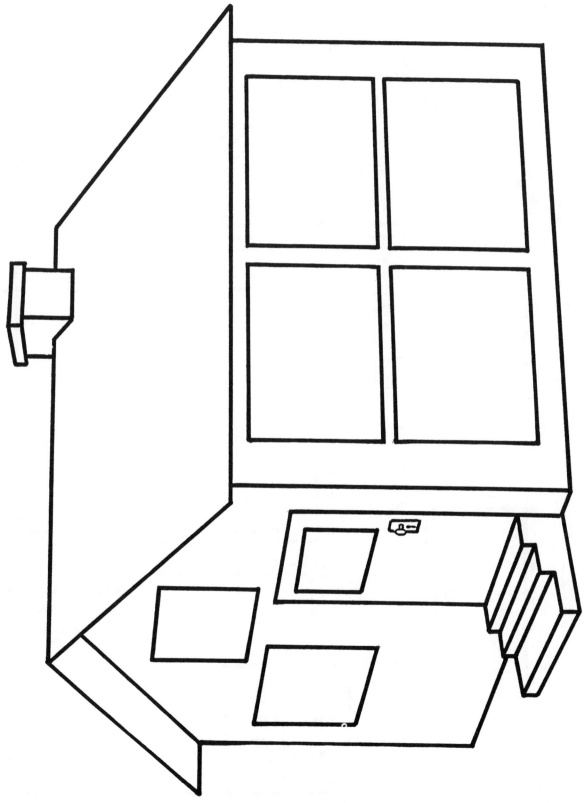

Name _____

Parts of a House

Discuss building a house from the bottom up. Include foundation, stairs, walls, roof, and chimney.

Instruct the children to color the parts of the house realistically, cut out the pieces and glue them to construction paper, following the model.

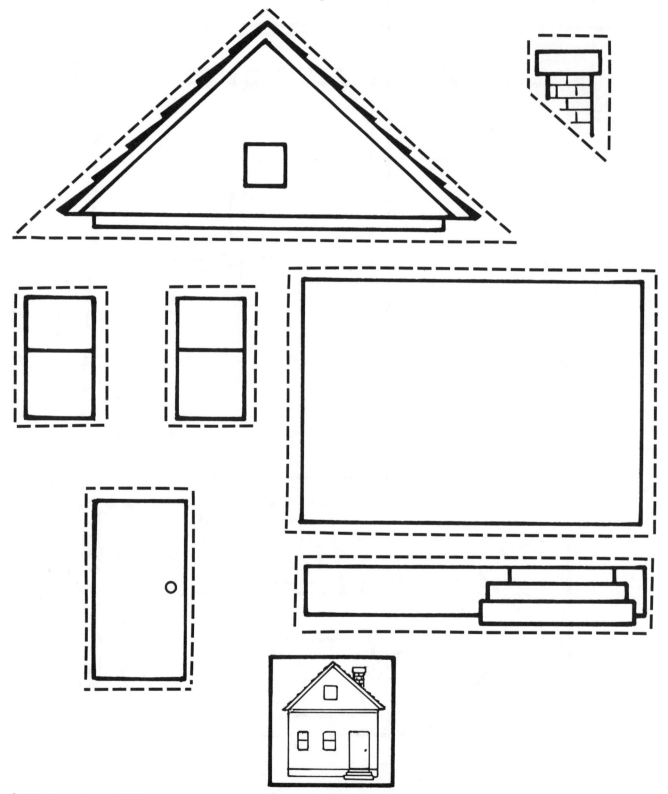

Name _____

Building a House

Give each child a copy of this page and a sheet of 12″ x 18″ construction paper, folded into fourths. Talk with them about building a house. Discuss foundation, studs, roof supports, walls, chimney, windows, and doors. Talk about the story shown here.

Have the children number each frame according to the sequence of events (1, 2, 3, 4), color the pictures appropriately (using consistent colors for the wall and roof in each frame), cut out, and glue the story pictures in correct sequence on the prefolded paper. Have each child tell the story, using complete sentences. Send the papers home for the children to share with their families.

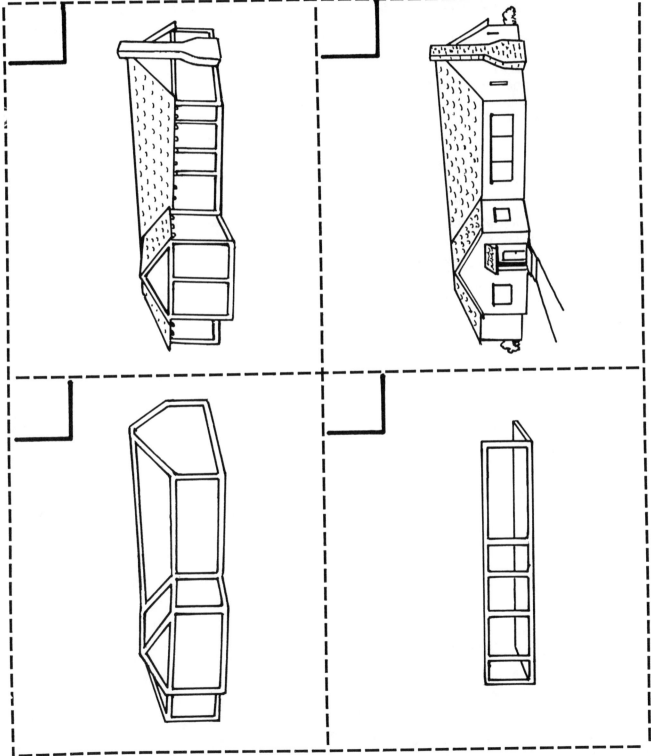

Furniture Pictures

Discuss furniture and appliances found in different rooms of a house.

Make Flashcards

Cut sheets of 9" x 12" construction paper into fourths, using a different color for each child, if possible. Each child should receive eighteen pieces.

Have each child realistically color all of the pictures on each of the furniture pages.

Have each child mount the pictures on the construction paper.

Use flashcards to:
    practice naming household items.
    play matching games.
    sort into appropriate rooms.

Complete Room Worksheet

Have each child:
    decide which room of the house to decorate.

    select, color, and cut out the items appropriate to the chosen room from the furniture and appliance pages.

    color or decorate the Room Worksheet, using wallpaper samples if desired.

    glue the furniture in place in the room.

Name _____

Furniture 1

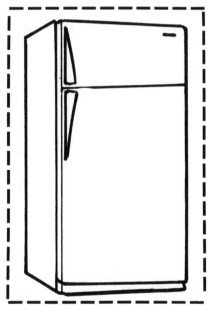

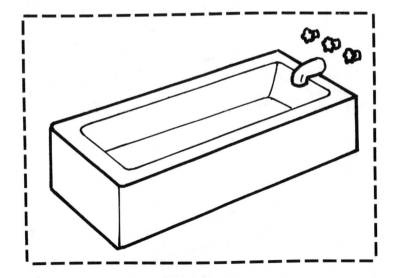

Name _____

Furniture 2

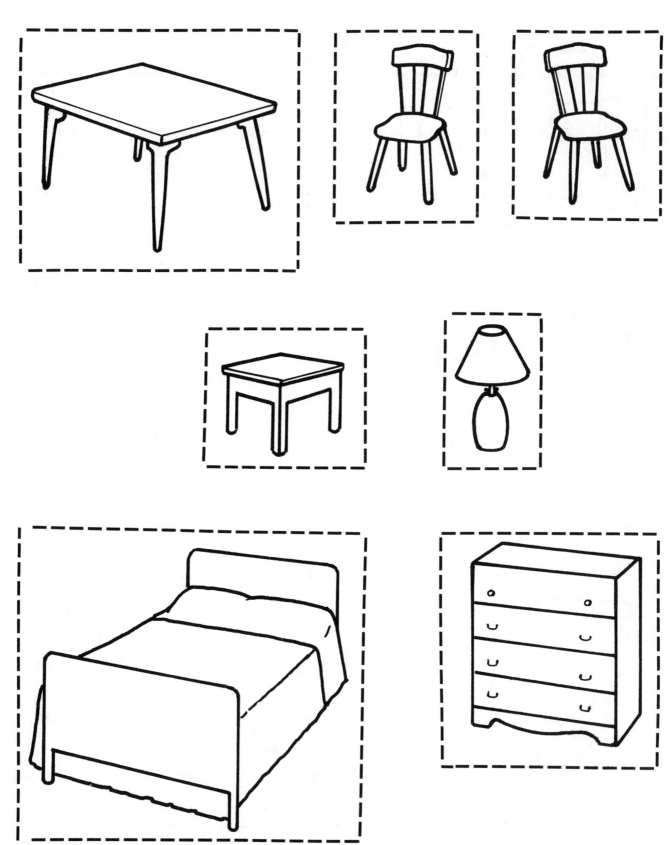

Name _____

Furniture 3

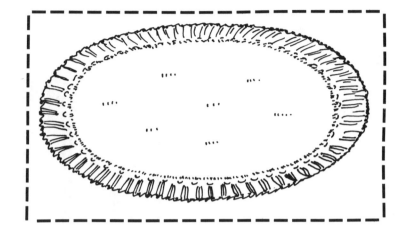

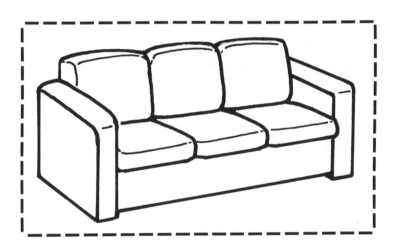

Name _____

Complete Room Worksheet

Name _____

Tools for the Toolbox

Talk with the children about tools as a category. Have them color, cut, and glue the tools on the Toolbox Worksheet.

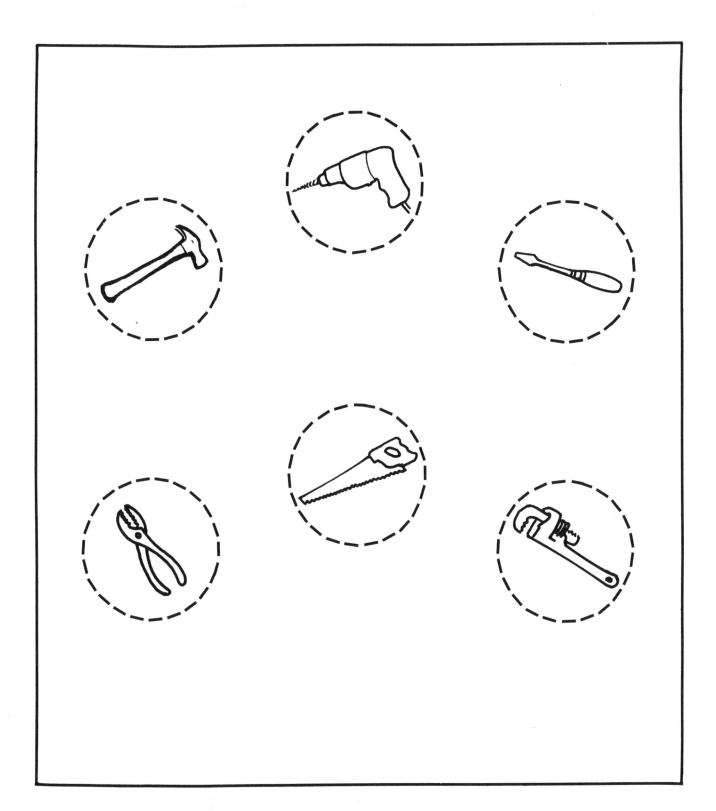

Name _____

Toolbox Worksheet

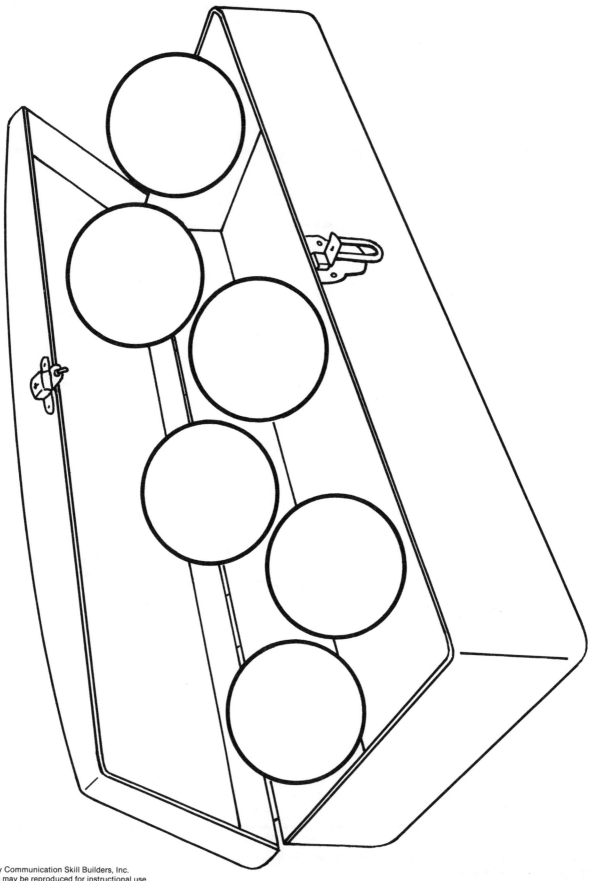

Name _____

Helping at Home

Talk with the children about helping at home. Have them each draw a picture about how they help at home. Have them each dictate a sentence about their picture and write it on the top of the paper.

Name _____

My Pet

Talk with the children about pets. Have them each draw a picture of the pet they have or would like to have on the end of the leash. Have them each dictate a sentence about their picture and write it on the top of the paper.

Name _____

A Special Gift

Talk with the children about giving and receiving a special gift. Have them each draw in the box a picture of a special gift they would like to give or receive. Have them each dictate a sentence about their picture and write it on the top of the paper.

Name _____

What Is In Your Pocket?

Talk with the children about imagining something in their pockets. Have them each draw a picture of what they imagined. Have them each dictate a sentence about their picture and write it on the top of the paper.

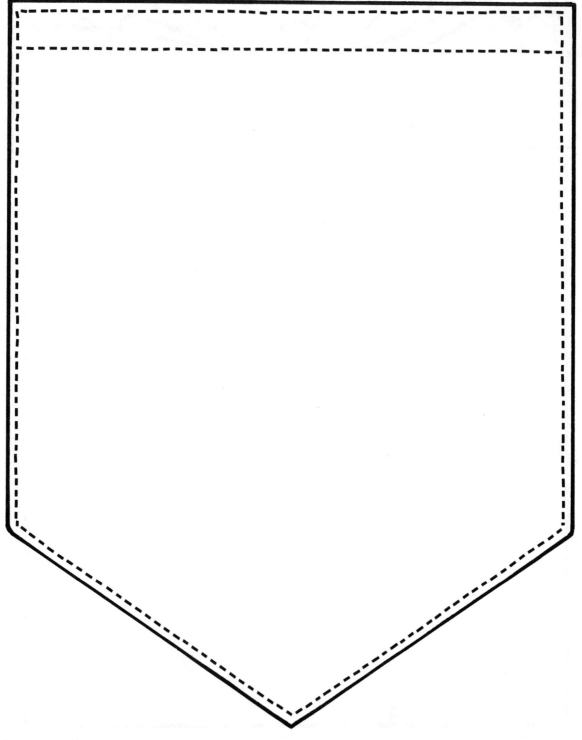

Name _____

Going Camping

Talk with the children about camping experiences. Give each child a copy of this page and a 12″ x 18″ sheet of construction paper, folded into fourths. Talk about the sequence of events in the story.

Have the children: number each frame, according to the sequence of events (1, 2, 3, 4); color the pictures appropriately (using consistent colors for the clothing, car, and tent in each frame); cut out; and glue the story pictures in correct sequence on the prefolded paper. Have each child tell the story in correct sequence, using complete sentences. Send the papers home for the children to share with their families.

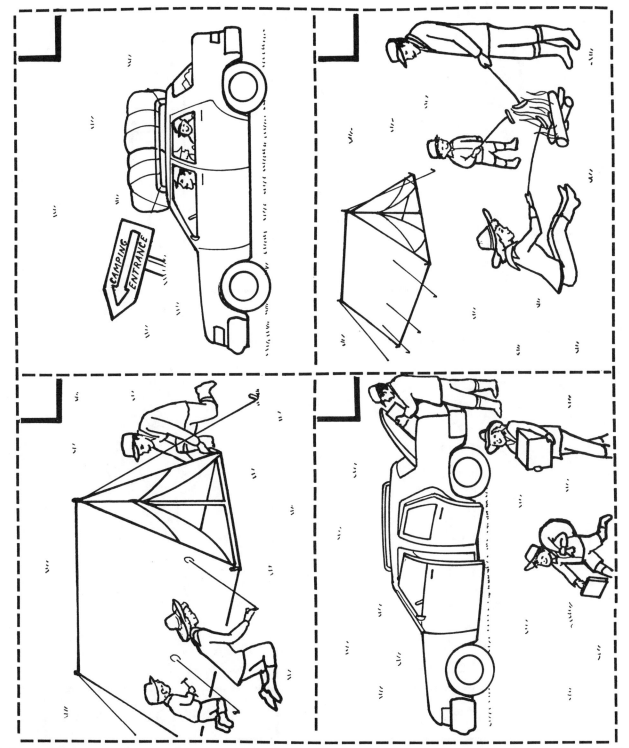

Name _____

People We See at School 1

Talk about all the important jobs there are at school. Discuss the personnel and the jobs they do. Include principal, teacher, speech pathologist, nurse, janitor or custodian, secretary, crossing guard, cafeteria worker, and librarian. Have the children color the pictures, cut them out, and add them to the School Building picture on page 36.

Teacher/Principal
Speech Pathologist

Principal/Teacher

Nurse

Janitor/Custodian

Name _____

People We See at School 2

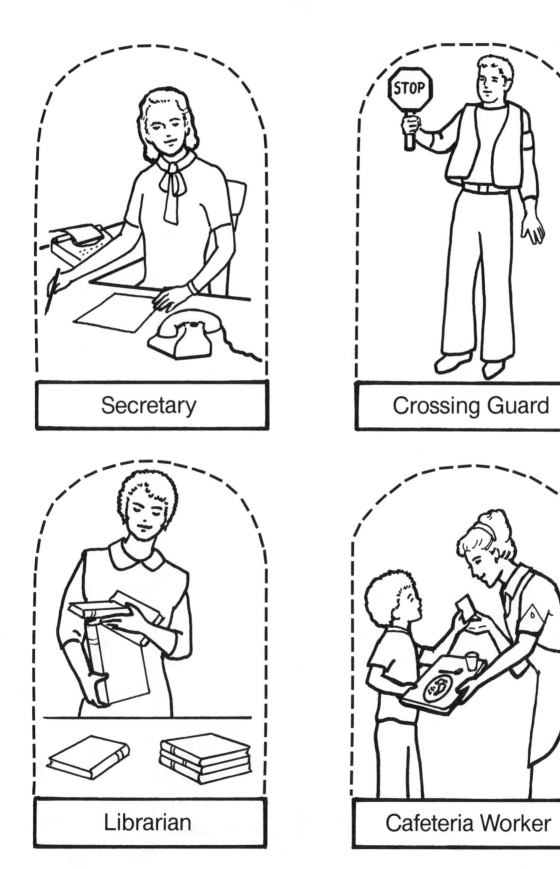

Secretary

Crossing Guard

Librarian

Cafeteria Worker

Name _____

School Building and Flag

Have the children:
color the school building using appropriate colors.

cut out the school building and mount it on a piece of construction paper.

color the flag accurately, cut it out, and place it on the school grounds. (The flag can be used with other buildings as well.)

color and add pictures from People We See at School.

add children from the Family Group (page 17).

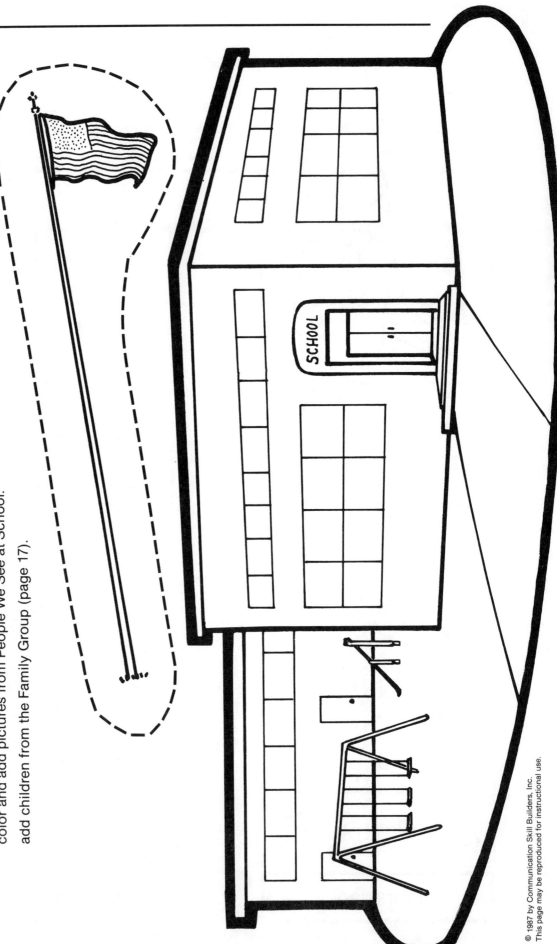

School Activity

Behavior at School—Rules

Five rules frequently used in a primary classroom are illustrated. They may be used to: make posters for the classroom showing expected behaviors.

mount in a take-home book telling the parents about behavior expected at school.

start a discussion of acceptable and unacceptable behaviors at school.

help the children make responsible choices.

General directions

After talking about the targeted behavior, discuss what is happening in the two pictures at the bottom of the page. Help the children select the scene that reflects the better behavior, color it, cut it out, and place it in the box entitled "What goes here?"

Coming into the Classroom

Talk with the children about the proper way to come into the classroom. Talk with them about what to do with coats and other belongings after they enter the room. Discuss the picture of the children entering the room. Point out coats and lunch boxes. Have the children color the picture.

Listening to Others

Talk with the children about listening to others. Have them color the picture of the teacher holding the book.

Raising Hand to Talk

Talk with the children about raising their hands to ask for permission to talk. Have them color the picture of the teacher talking to the children.

Cleaning Up

Talk with the children about cleaning up and being responsible for materials. Have them color the picture of the children painting.

Taking Turns

Talk with the children about taking turns. Have them color the picture of the water fountain.

Name _____

Coming into the Classroom

What goes here?

Name _____

Listening to Others

What goes here?

Name _____

Raising Hand to Talk

What goes here?

Name _____

Cleaning Up

What goes here?

42 • SCHOOL ACTIVITY: RULES

Name _____

Taking Turns

What goes here?

Name _____

Following School Rules

Talk with the children about following school rules. Have them each draw a picture of themselves following a school rule. Then have them each dictate a sentence about their picture and write it on the top of the paper.

Lunch at School

Talk with the children about buying lunch at school.

Give each child a copy of the Lunch at School page and a sheet of 12″ x 18″ construction paper, folded into fourths.

Talk about the story.

Have the children:

number each frame according to the sequence of events (1, 2, 3, 4).

color the pictures appropriately, using consistent colors for the clothing of the girl who is buying lunch.

cut out and glue the story pictures in correct sequence on the prefolded paper.

each tell the story, using complete sentences.

take their papers home to share with their families.

Name _____

Lunch at School

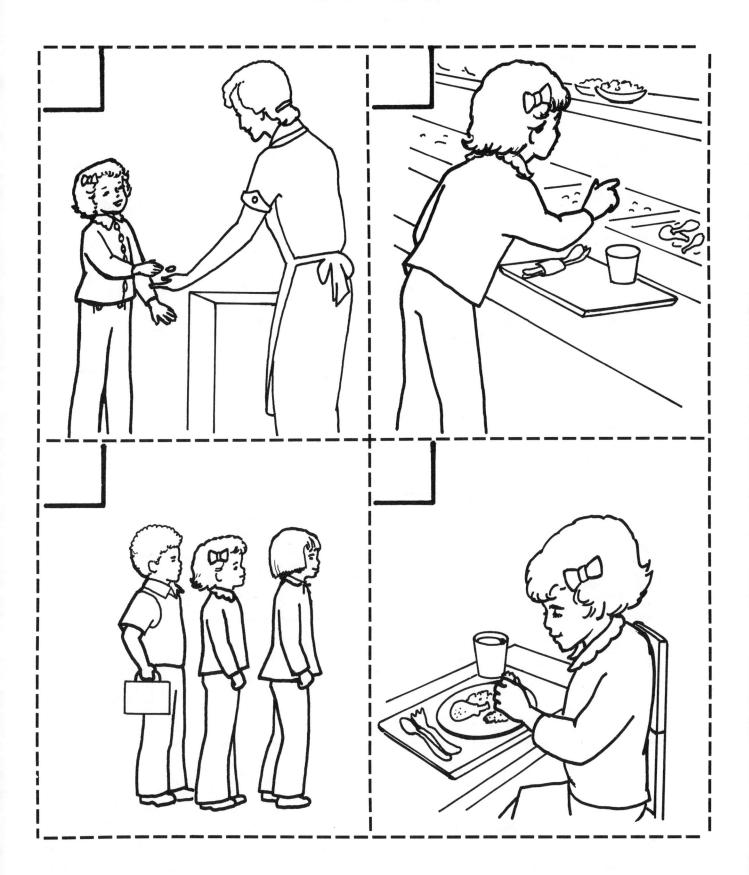

Name _____

Same—School Supplies

Review with the children the meaning of same.

Have the children name all of the school items in Row 1, going from left to right. Have them color the two items that are the same. This activity helps generalize the concept same.

Repeat the directions for Rows 2 through 6.

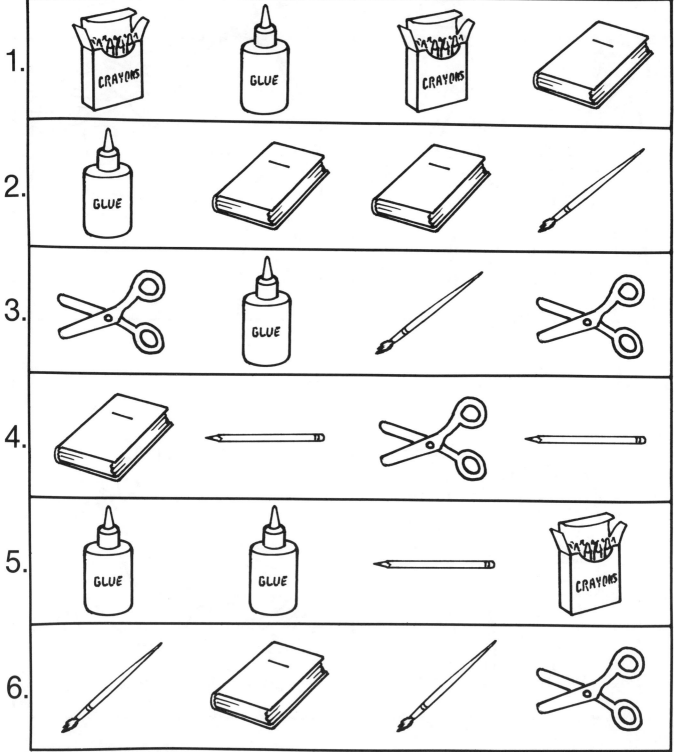

Name _____

Different—School Supplies

Review with the children the meaning of different.

Have them name all of the school items in Row 1, going from left to right. Have them color the item that is different in Row 1. This activity helps generalize the concept different.

Repeat the directions for Rows 2 through 6.

1.

2.

3.

4.

5.

6.

Learning About the Community
Bulletin Board Activity

The materials in this section may be used in many ways and for many activities. Building a bulletin board is one way to organize and integrate all of the information about the community, as well as to reinforce concepts and vocabulary, demonstrate relationships, and provide a means for self-expression in the classroom. Building a bulletin-board town is something in which each child can and should participate. The town is made of many pieces that every child can successfully construct and see related to the whole. As new parts of the town are added, awareness will grow in the children. They will have more questions for their parents as they travel together; they will learn where the fire station is in their neighborhood; they will return to school asking to add things to the town; they will be aware of spatial relationships as they are placing their buildings, vehicles, people, and signs on the streets.

Materials
> bulletin board
> white butcher paper
> opaque projector
> black waterproof marker
> watercolor paints
> paintbrushes, ½" or 1" wide
> construction paper
> crayons
> pencils
> scissors
> map (page 52)
> buildings (pages 54-60)
> vehicles (pages 61-67)
> people (pages 68-69)

Preparing the background
Cover the bulletin board with butcher paper.

Project the map onto the bulletin board. Trace, using the waterproof marker.

Mix watercolors and paint sky, streets, and ground. (NOTE: This background may be reused.)

Preparing and placing buildings
Making a home for each child, Option 1:
Encourage the children to draw their own homes.

Talk about the homes in terms of squares, rectangles, and triangles. (This is a good time for review and generalization.) Draw samples on the chalkboard.

Give each child a pencil and a 4½" x 6" piece of white construction paper. Have the children:
> draw their homes, following one or more of the samples.
> add windows, doors, and other details.
> color the drawings realistically.

Outline the drawings and trace over all the pencil lines with a black marker. Cut out drawings, including the black outline, and place on the bulletin board.

Option 2:
Send home two pieces of 4½" x 6" paper, one for practice and one for the final drawing. Include a note asking the parents to help the child complete a picture of their home on the attached piece of construction paper. See sample note on page 53. (This activity provides an opportunity for parents and children to work and talk together. Parents often become interested in the project, coming to school to see what the bulletin board looks like and to admire their own contribution.)

Outline the drawings and trace over all pencil lines with a black marker. Cut out the drawings (including the black outline) and post on the bulletin-board town.

Option 3:
Give each child the picture of the house on page 54. Have the children color the picture to look like their own homes.

Outline the houses with the black marker. Cut them out, including the black outlines, and place on the bulletin board.

Adding other buildings
Discuss buildings and their different functions and shapes.

Decide with the children what other buildings to have around the town. Suggest police station, fire station, post office, hospital, airport, hotel, stores, office building, offices, school (page 36), restaurant, gas station . . .

Copy the buildings from pages 54-60. Have each child color a special building and cut it out, including the black outline.

Discuss each building, its function, and where it should be located. Place each building appropriately on the bulletin board.

Preparing and placing vehicles
Making a vehicle for each child, Option 1:
Encourage each child to draw a family vehicle. Talk about the vehicles in terms of body, wheels, front, and back. Draw samples on the chalkboard.

Give each child a pencil and a 4½" x 6" piece of white construction paper. Have each child:
    draw the vehicle, using one or more samples.
    add details.
    color the vehicle to look like a family vehicle.
    put a driver in the vehicle.

Outline the vehicles and trace over all the pencil lines with a black marker.

Cut them out, including the black outline, and place on the bulletin board.

Option 2:
Send home two 4½" x 6" pieces of paper, one for practice and one for the final drawing. Include a note (sample on page 53) asking the parents to help child complete a picture of a family vehicle, including a driver, on the attached piece of construction paper.

Outline the vehicles with a black marker and cut them out, including the black outline. Place on the bulletin board.

Option 3:
Have each child select a picture of a vehicle from pages 61-62 and color it to look like a family vehicle. Have each child put a driver in the vehicle.

Outline the vehicles with a black marker.

Cut them out, including the black outline, and place on the bulletin board.

Adding special vehicles
Discuss vehicles and their different functions and shapes.

Decide with the chidren what other vehicles to have around the town. Suggest police car, fire truck, mail truck, ambulance, airplane, garbage truck, school bus . . .

Copy the vehicles from pages 63-67. Have each child color and cut out a special vehicle. Discuss each vehicle and its function. Place each vehicle appropriately on the bulletin board.

Adding people
Decide with the children what people to have around the town. Discuss various occupations. Copy the people you choose from pages 68-69. Also use the school personnel from pages 34-35, and the family members from pages 16-17.

Have the children color, cut, and place the people in appropriate places on the bulletin board.

Adding signs and other details
Decide with the children other things to have around the town.

Copy the signs you are using from page 70. Have the children color, cut out, and place them on the bulletin board.

Have the children add trees, pets . . .

Map

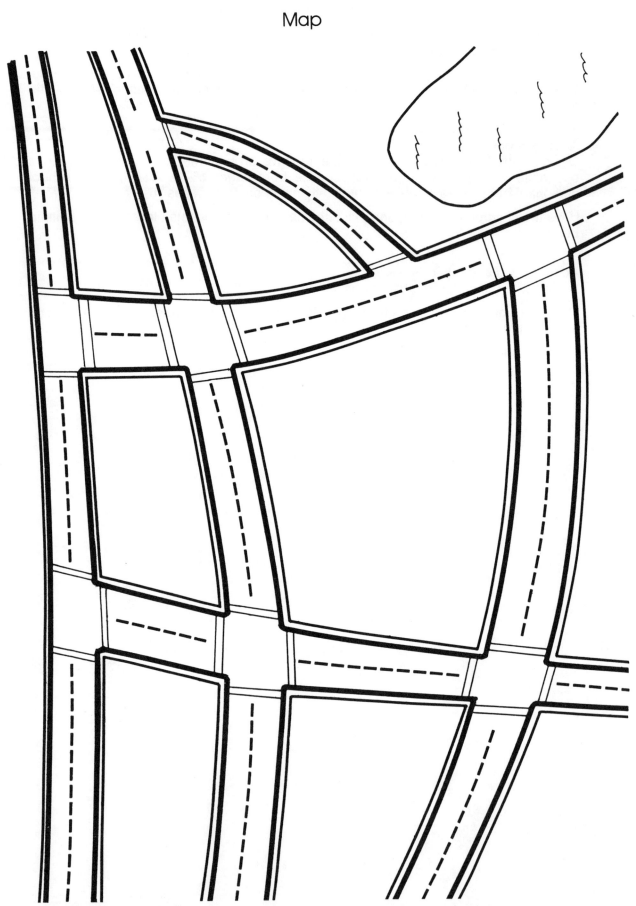

Date _____

Dear Parents,

We are making a map of our town on the bulletin board at school. Each child is going to put up a picture of the family vehicle. Please help your child draw and color a vehicle on the attached paper to look like the one your family uses. (The second piece of paper is for a practice drawing.) We will cut out the drawing and put it up on our bulletin board.

Please return the completed vehicle by _____

Thank you,

_____

- -

Date _____

Dear Parents,

We are making a map of our town on the bulletin board at school. Each child is going to put up a picture of home. Please help your child draw your home on the attached paper and color it realistically. (The second piece of paper is for a practice drawing.) We will cut out the drawing and put it up on our bulletin board.

Please return the completed drawing by _____

Thank you,

_____

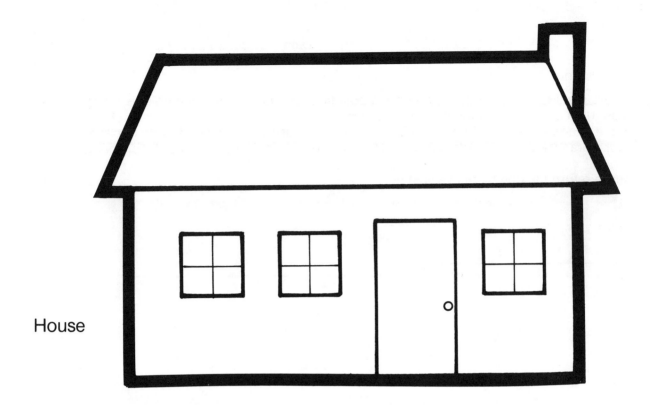

House

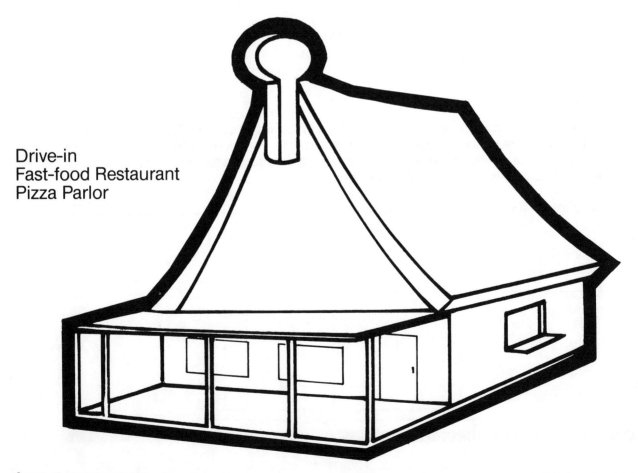

Drive-in
Fast-food Restaurant
Pizza Parlor

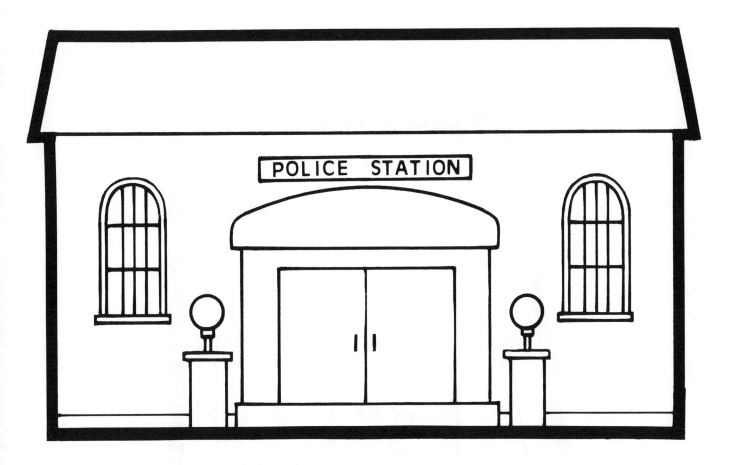

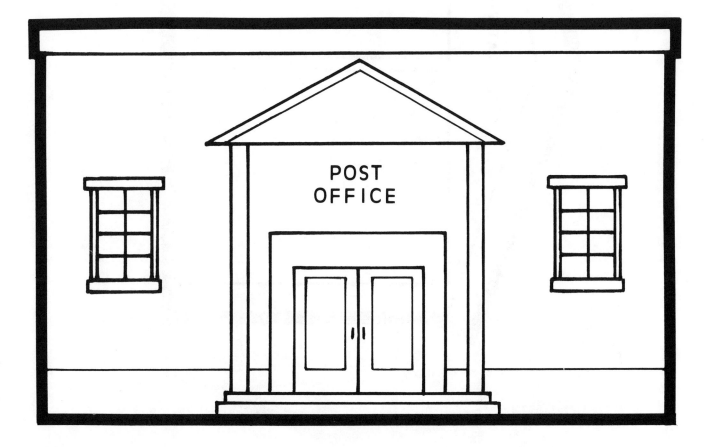

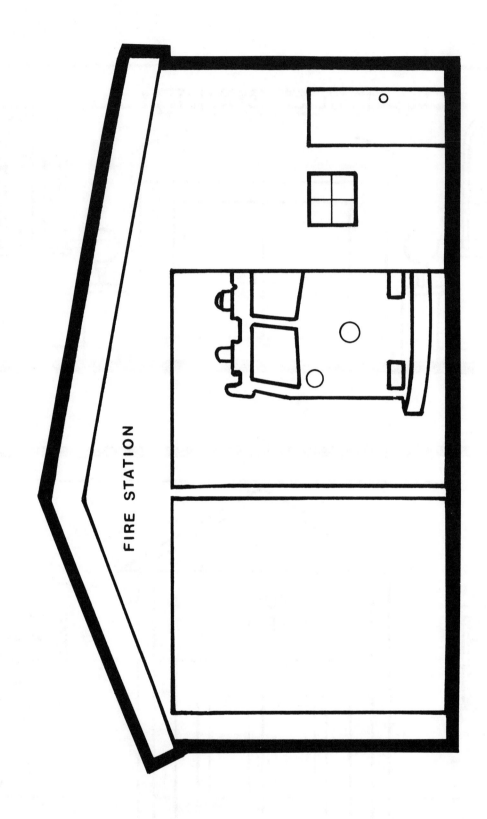

FIRE STATION

Office Building
Hotel
Apartment House
Hospital

Vary the size and shape of this building by cutting on the heavy lines.

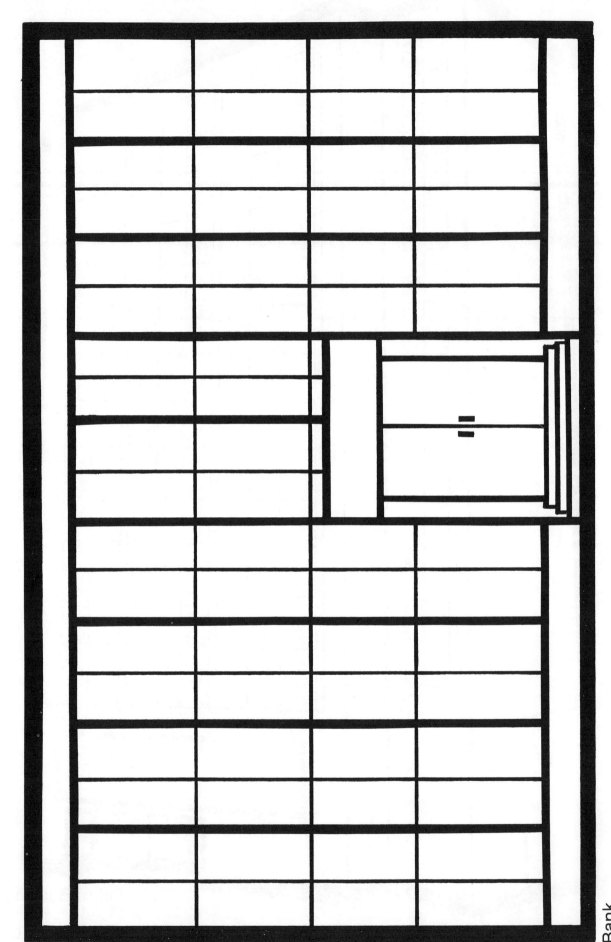

Bank
Office Building

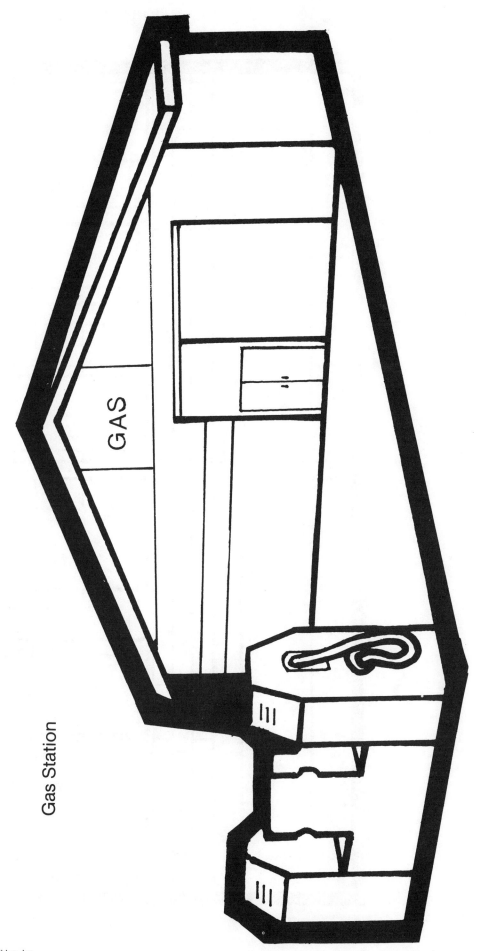

Gas Station

Shopping Center

May be used as single or multiple units.

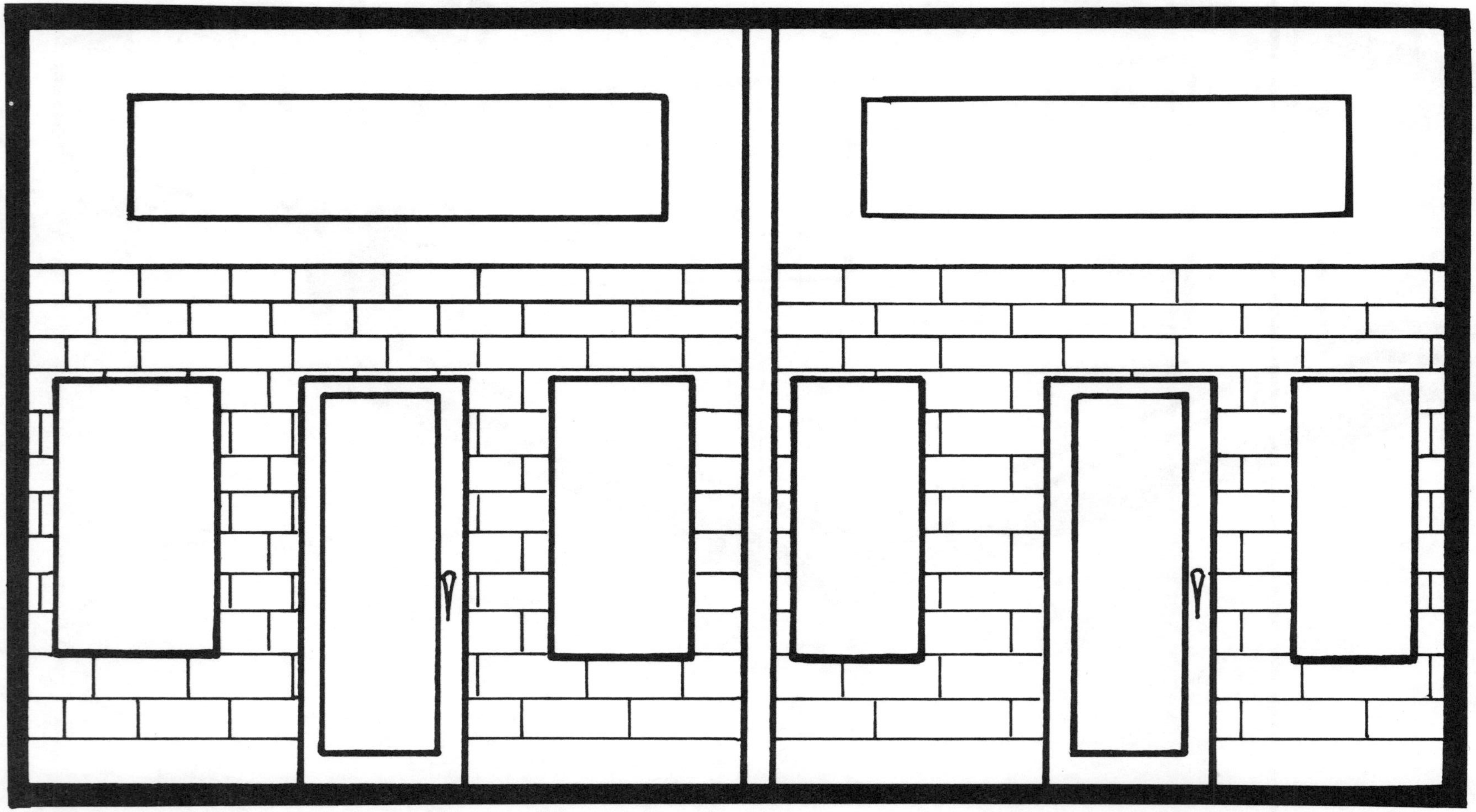

Offices

Laundromat

Shops

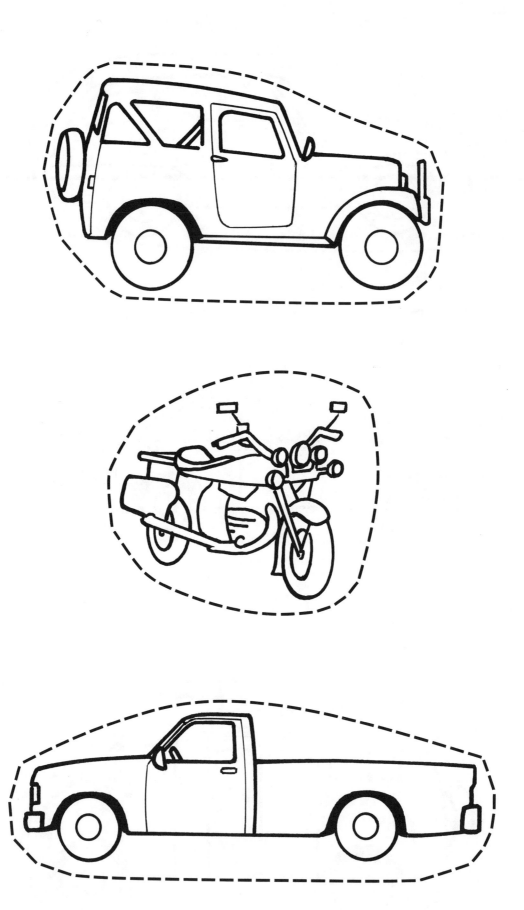

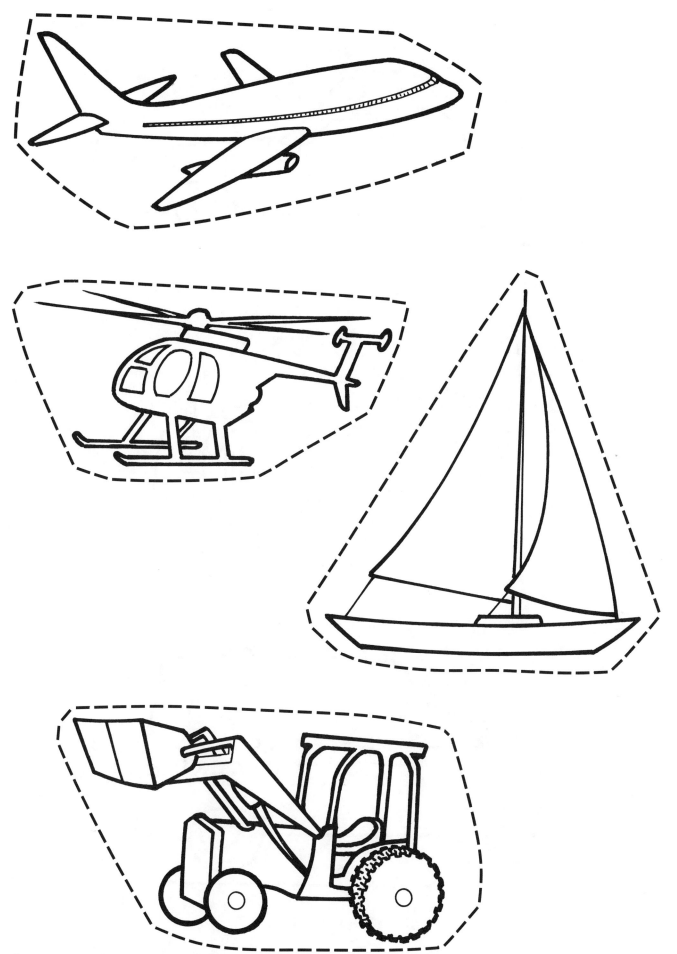

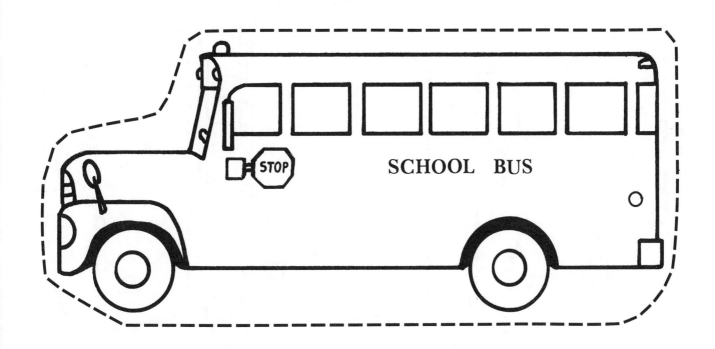

SCHOOL BUS

STOP

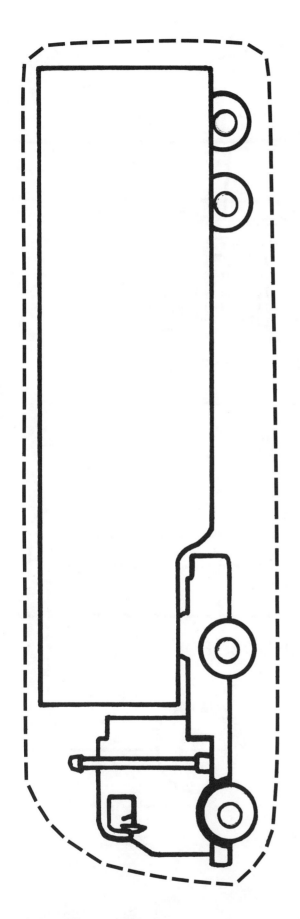

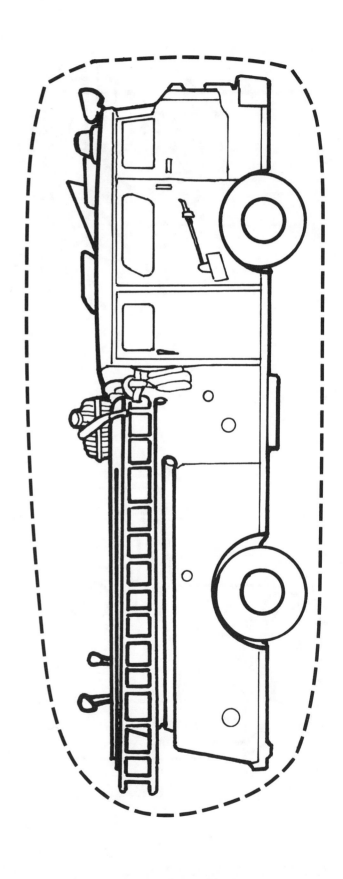

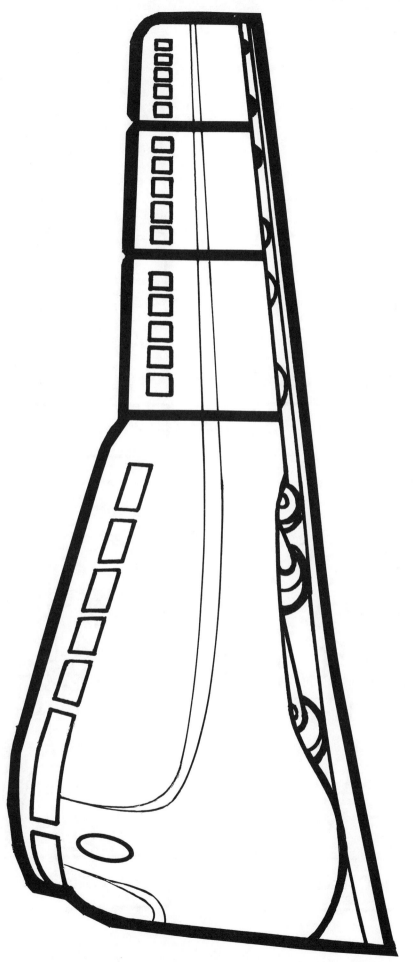

Mail Carrier

Firefighter

Garbage Collector

Police Officer

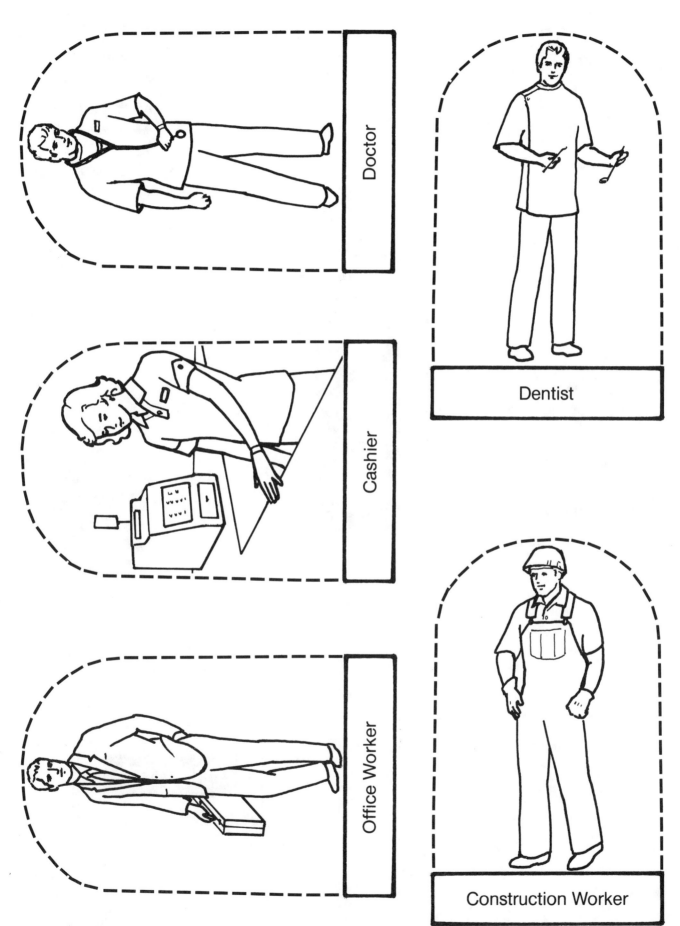

Doctor

Cashier

Office Worker

Dentist

Construction Worker

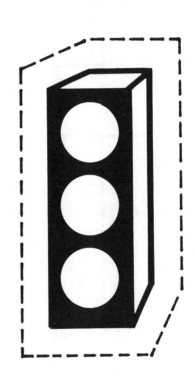

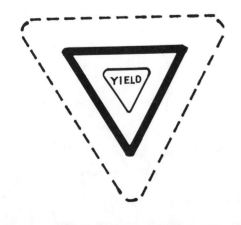

COMMUNITY ACTIVITY: OTHER THINGS • 71

Additional "Around Town" Activities

Community Helpers
While studying the individual community helpers, have the children make a picture of the helper, the helper's vehicle, and the helper's related building (such as firefighter, fire truck, and fire station).

Vehicles
Have the children color and mount the pictures of vehicles on construction paper cut as flashcards. Have them select vehicles by particular properties, sort them into groups, and discuss similarities and differences. This makes a good home project.

Occupations
Have the children color and mount the pictures of community workers on construction paper cut as flashcards. Have them group workers and discuss similarities and differences among occupations. This makes a good home project.

Combinations
Have the children select the occupations flashcards and vehicle flashcards that go together. This could be made into a card game.

Dioramas
Have the children use the buildings, vehicles and/or people in a diorama of a town. Mix and match the items so all dioramas will be different.

A Book About . . .
Have the children make up a book or books about vehicles, buildings, community helpers, stores . . . Make one book for the classroom or individual ones to take home.

Buildings and Their Purposes
Have the children select a building to tell about and to illustrate.

Careers
Have the children talk about and illustrate what they would like to be when they grow up.

Milk-Carton Town
Have the children make three-dimensional buildings from small milk or juice cartons. Select and reproduce the buildings to be used. Have the children color and cut them out. Glue the buildings onto construction paper for reinforcement and cut them out. To make backs, trace onto another piece of paper and cut out. Glue a matching front and back to a carton and staple the sides together. These buildings will stand up nicely on the table or floor, and the children can use miniature cars to drive around them. Color and cut out the people, including the stands, and place them around town. Color and cut out the vehicles.

Community Activities

Hats for Police Officer and Firefighter
Give each child a copy of the hat picture on page 74 or 75. Have each child color and cut out the hat. Mount the hat across the center to a 2" wide tagboard strip. Fit the strip to the child's head and staple ends.

Assembling a Car
Give each child a copy of page 76. Have the children:
    color the car parts appropriately, watching out for the windows.
    cut the paper on the center line.
    cut out the parts and glue them where they belong on the car.
    color the rest of the car.

Let's Make a Hot Air Balloon
Give each child a copy of the balloon picture on page 77. Discuss hot air balloons and show pictures, if available. Talk about the exciting designs that decorate hot air balloons. Ask them to color their balloons, making them all different. Put the child's name on the back of the paper and display the balloons on the bulletin board.

What Doesn't Belong? (Community Workers)
Give each child a copy of pages 78-79. Talk about the community workers shown and the things they need to do their jobs. Discuss each of the boxes on the page, and instruct the children to cross out the object that is not associated with the person in the box. Have the children color the two appropriate objects and the community workers in each box.

Name _____

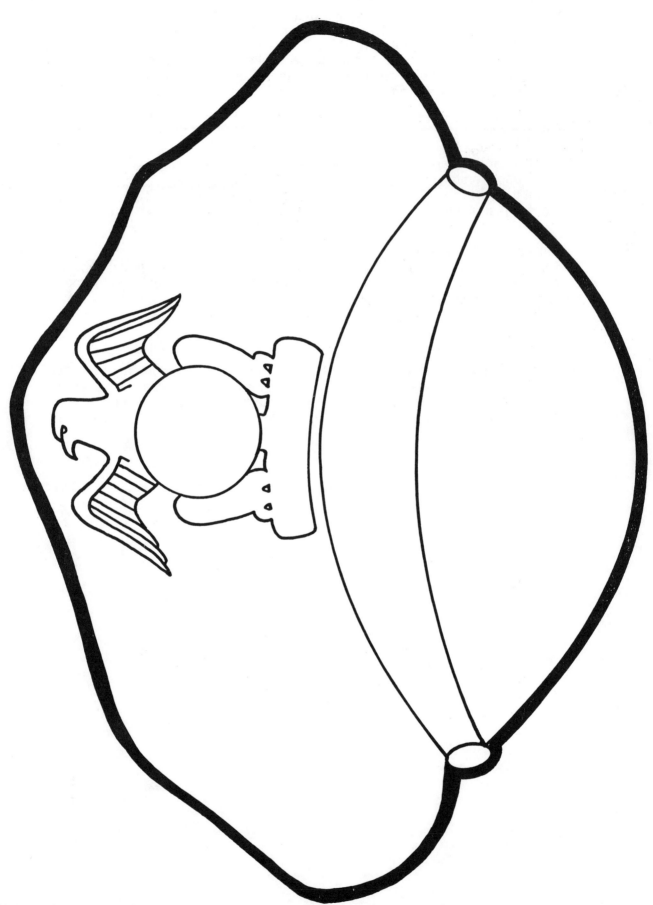

Name _____

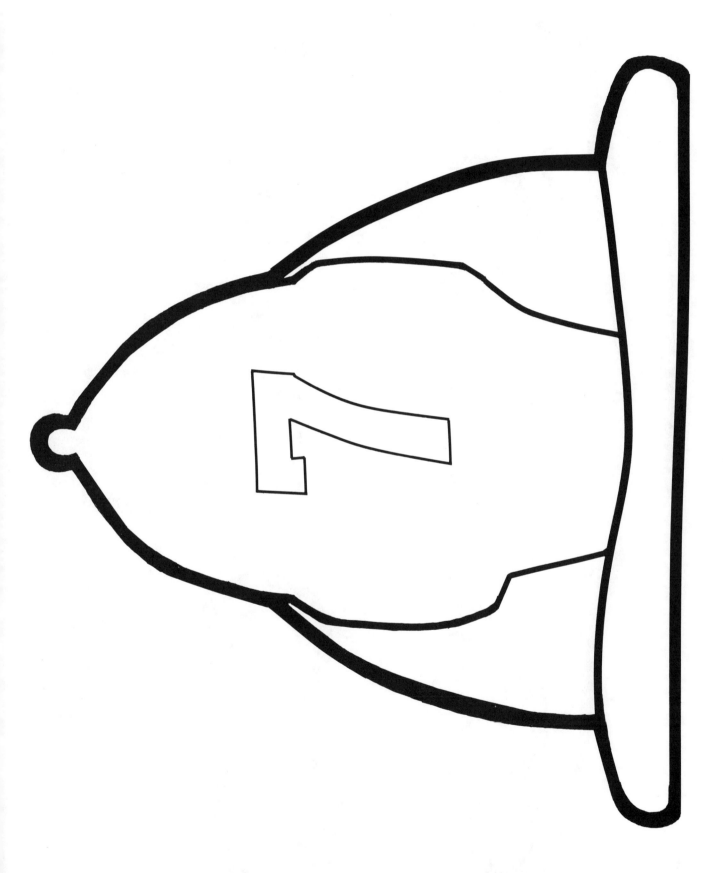

Name _____

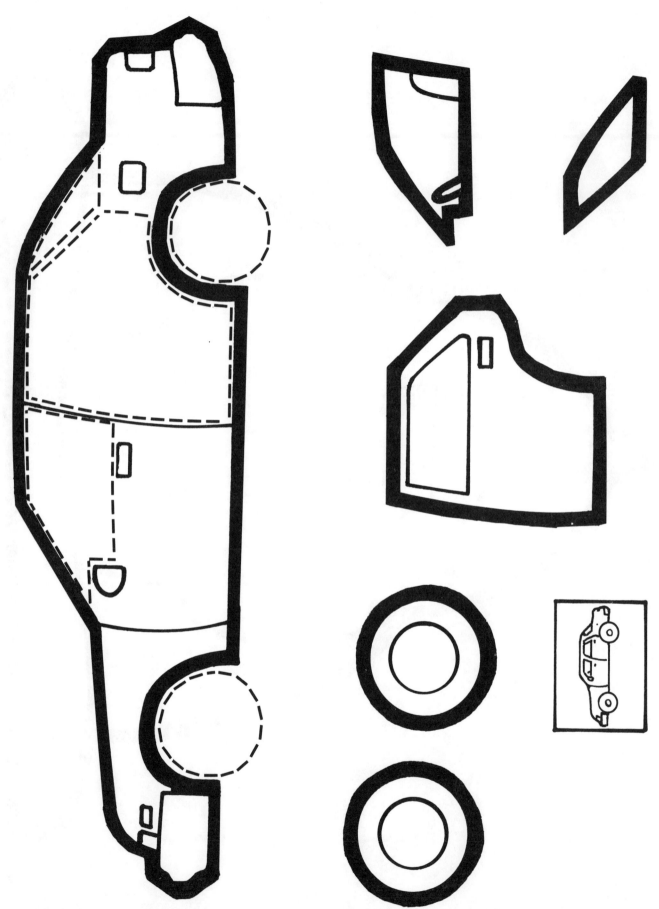

Name _____

Name _____

What Doesn't Belong?

Name _____

What Doesn't Belong?

Classification Activities

Let's Go Shopping

Grocery Store
Give each child a copy of the Store Worksheet and the Grocery Store sheet on page 82.

Talk with the children about categories. Discuss items you would find in a grocery store and the items shown. Have the children color the sign and the items that belong in a grocery store.

Have them cut out the sign and glue it to the counter, and cut out the colored items and glue them to the circles on the shelves.

Use the same worksheet and instructions for:
    Pet Store (page 83)
    Clothing Store (page 84)
    Toy Store (page 85)
    Bakery (page 86)
    Drugstore (page 87)

Name _____

Store Worksheet

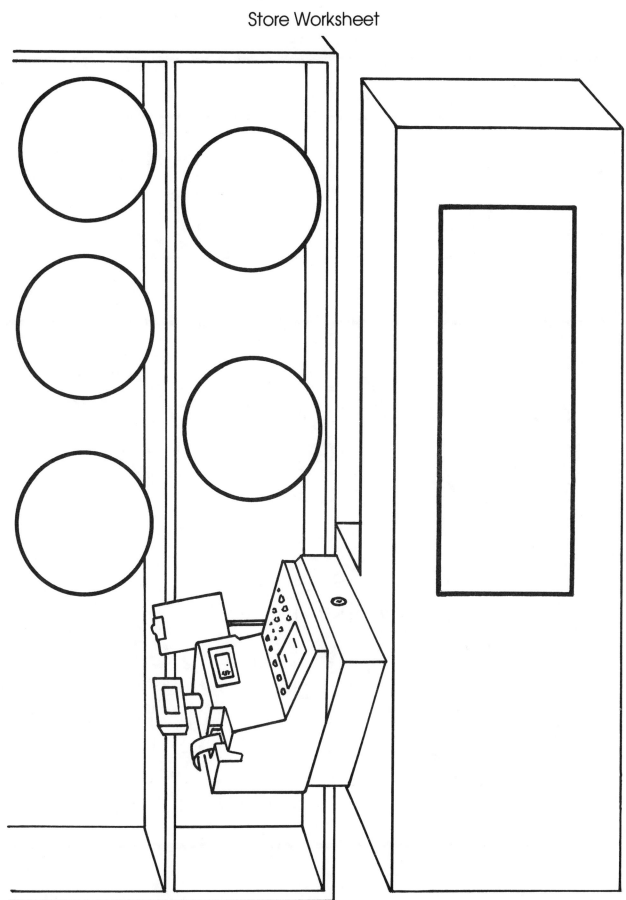

Name _____

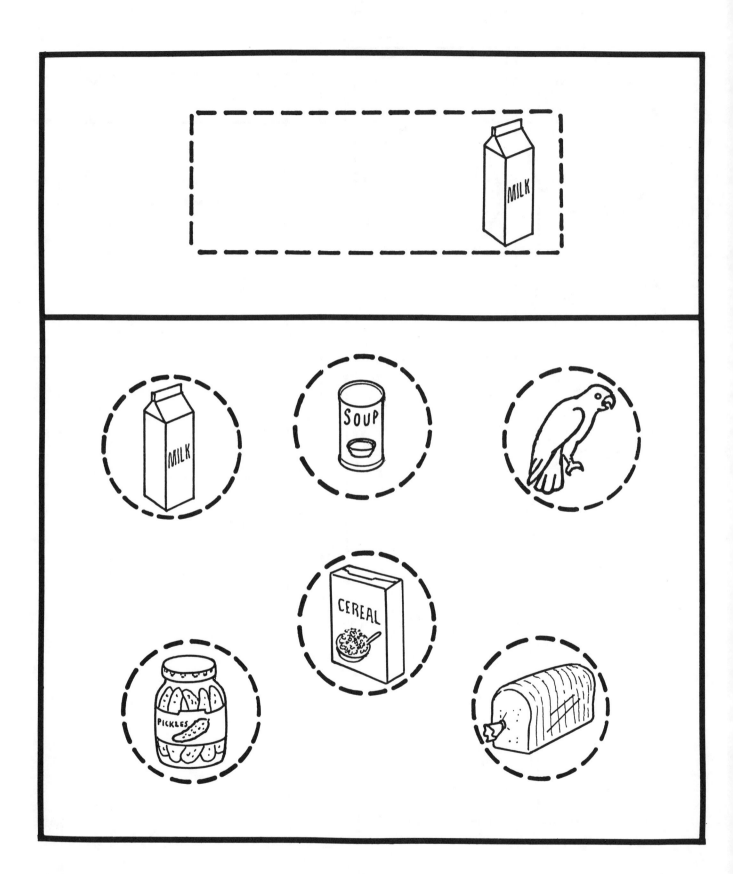

Name _____

Name _____

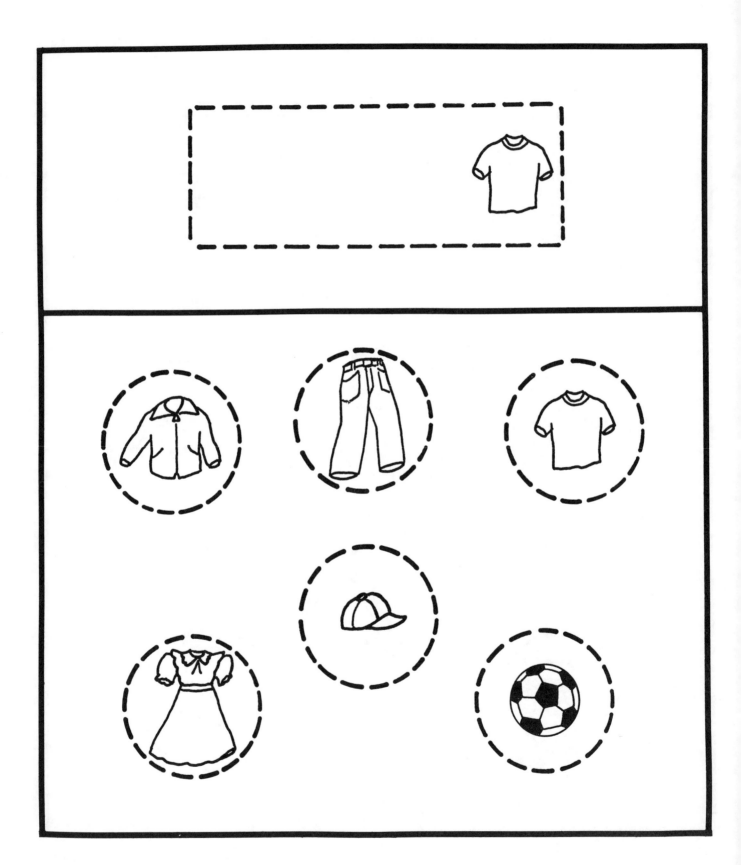

Name _____

Name _____

Name _____

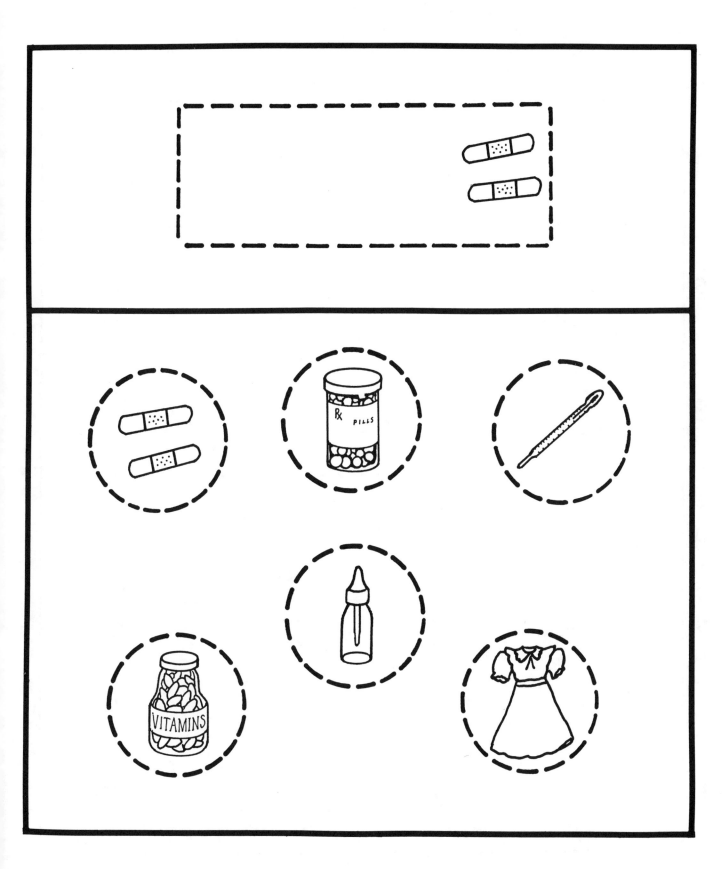

Name _____

Categories—The Same

Talk with the children about items that belong in the same category. Have the children name the items in Row 1, from left to right. Have them color all of the items that belong in the same category. Repeat the activity for Rows 2 through 6.

1.

2.

3.

4.

5.

6.

Name _____

Categories—Not the Same

Talk with the children about items that do not belong in the same category. Have the children name the items in Row 1, from left to right. Have them circle and color the item that does not belong in the same category as the other items in the row. Repeat the activity for Rows 2 through 6.

1.

2.

3.

4.

5.

6.

Buying a New Pair of Shoes

Talk with the children about shopping.

Give each child a copy of the next page and a 12" x 18" sheet of construction paper, folded into fourths.

Talk about the story sequence on the page. Have the children:

number each frame according to the sequence of events (1, 2, 3, 4).

color the pictures appropriately, using consistent colors for clothing in each frame.

cut out and glue the story pictures in correct sequence on the prefolded paper.

tell the story in correct sequence, using complete sentences.

take their papers home to share with their families.

Name _____

Buying a New Pair of Shoes

Hot and Cold

Talk with the children about the meaning of hot and cold. Discuss the pictures on this page, using hot and cold. Have the children color the pictures (optional), cut them out, and glue them in the corresponding columns on the Hot and Cold Worksheet.

Name _____

Hot and Cold Worksheet

Hot	Cold

Hard and Soft

Talk with the children about the meaning of hard and soft. Discuss the pictures on this page, using hard and soft. Have the children color the pictures (optional), cut them out, and glue them in the corresponding columns on the Hard and Soft Worksheet.

Name _____

Hard and Soft Worksheet

Hard	Soft

Wet and Dry

Talk with the children about the meaning of wet and dry. Discuss the pictures on this page, using wet and dry. Have the children color the pictures (optional), cut them out, and glue them in the corresponding columns on the Wet and Dry Worksheet.

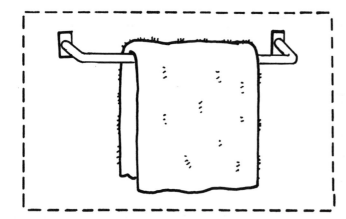

Name _____

Wet and Dry Worksheet

Wet	Dry

Empty and Full

Talk with the children about the meaning of empty and full. Discuss the pictures on this page, using empty and full. Have the children color the pictures (optional), cut them out, and glue them in the corresponding columns on the Empty and Full Worksheet.

Name _____

Empty and Full Worksheet

Empty	Full

Rough and Smooth

Talk with the children about the meaning of rough and smooth. Discuss the pictures on this page, using rough and smooth. Have the children color the pictures (optional), cut them out, and glue them in the corresponding columns on the Rough and Smooth Worksheet.

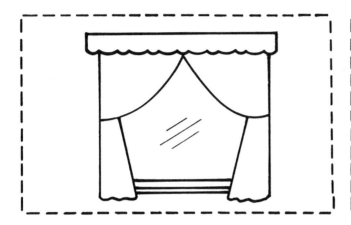

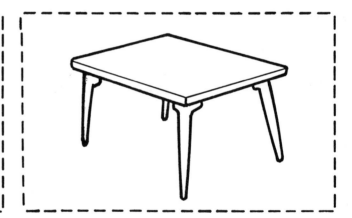

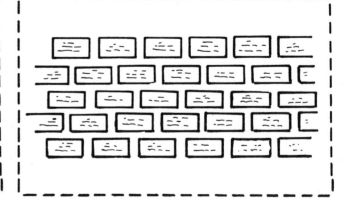

Name _____

Rough and Smooth Worksheet

Rough	Smooth

Real and Make-Believe

Talk with the children about the meaning of real and make-believe. Discuss the pictures on this page, using real and make-believe. Have the children color the pictures (optional), cut them out, and glue them in the corresponding columns on the Real and Make-Believe Worksheet.

Name _____

Real and Make-Believe Worksheet

Real	Make-Believe

Crayon-Resist Monster

Give each of the children a monster face. Instruct them to color all of the features heavily. Each child should use a different color.

Have them each choose a watercolor to paint over the entire mask. The paint will be absorbed only in the uncolored areas. When the masks are dry, cut out and post on a bulletin board.

Have the children describe their masks, to be guessed by someone in the group. Talk about giving enough information to make a guess possible. Have the other children listen to see if they can guess which mask is being described.

After they have each described their own mask for the group, they may describe others to be guessed.

Crayon-Resist Monster

Name _____

Behind

Talk with the children about the meaning of behind. Have them describe the two pictures in Row 1. Instruct them to color the picture that shows behind. Repeat the activity for Rows 2 through 5.

1.

2.

3.

4.

5.

Name _____

Around

Talk with the children about the meaning of around. Have them describe the two pictures in Row 1. Instruct them to color the picture that shows around. Repeat the activity for Rows 2 through 5.

1.

2.

3.

4.

5.

Name _____

Beside

Talk with the children about the meaning of beside. Have them describe the two pictures in Row 1. Instruct them to color the picture that shows beside. Repeat the activity for Rows 2 through 5.

1.

2.

3.

4.

5.

Name _____

Through

Talk with the children about the meaning of through. Have them describe the two pictures in Row 1. Instruct them to color the picture that shows through. Repeat the activity for Rows 2 through 5.

1.

2.

3.

4.

5.

The Three States of Water

Solid, Liquid, Gas

Talk with the children about:
  solids, such as furniture, blocks, and walls.
  liquids, such as milk, orange juice, and water.
  gases, such as air in a tire or in a hot air balloon, or smoke from a fire.

Explain that water can be a solid, a liquid, or a gas. Do an experiment to show this to the group.

EXPERIMENT

Materials
  three ice cubes
  hot plate
  small pan
  water glass
  hand mirror (cold)

Procedure
1. Show the children the ice cubes. Point out that they are cold and hard. Put them in the glass and in the pan to demonstrate that they have a shape of their own and are solids.

2. Place the ice cubes in the pan and melt them on the hot plate. Show the pan as the cubes melt, pointing out that there is some liquid and some solid in the pan.

3. As soon as the ice has melted (before it is too hot), pour the water into a glass. Show how the liquid takes on the shape of the container (pan to glass, glass to pan). Remind the class that a liquid has no shape of its own.

4. Put the water back in the pan and heat until steam rises from the water. Explain that the water is turning into steam (or into a gas).

5. Catch some of the steam on a cold mirror to show that it is water.

6. Continue heating until all the water is gone. Explain that the water has become a gas and is now part of the gas that is all around the room.

Conclusion: Water can be a solid, a liquid, or a gas.

Review the experiment and have the children complete the Three States of Water Worksheet:
  Instruct the children to cut out the items below the dotted line.

  Discuss the three pictures.

  Have the children arrange the pictures as follows:
    In the top box, put how the water looked at the beginning. If necessary, remind them that it was hard and cold, and was called a solid.

    In the middle box, put how the water looked second or next. If necessary, remind them that it was warm, had no shape of its own, and was called a liquid.

    In the bottom box, put how the water looked at the end of the experiment. If necessary, remind them that it was hot, had no shape of its own, and was called a gas.

Name _____

The Three States of Water

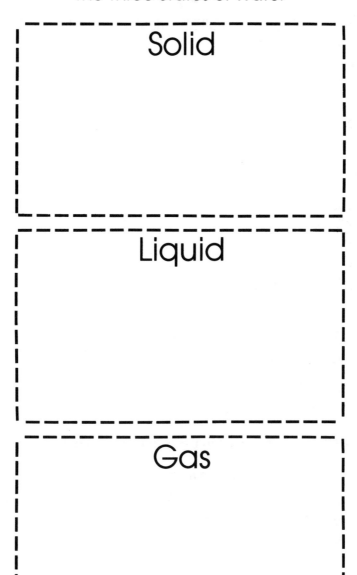

Solid

Liquid

Gas

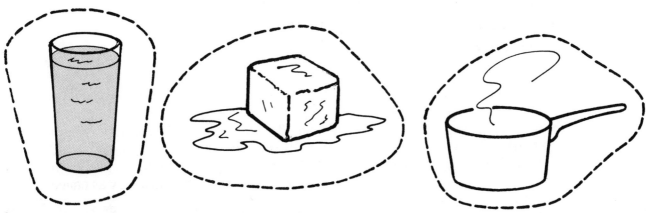

Following Directions

Directions may be given singly or in multiples, depending on the level of the group. For a different lesson, change or expand the directions.

Complete the House (page 113)
> Draw a tree next to the house.
>
> Color the door red.
>
> Color the roof brown.
>
> Put windows in the house.
>
> Put clouds in the sky.

A Pretty Teddy Bear (page 114)
> Color the teddy bear brown.
>
> Color his eyes and nose black.
>
> Color his bow green.
>
> Put an orange ball next to him.

Bookcase (page 115—this drawing can be used many times.)
> Put three books on the middle shelf. Color them brown.
>
> Put a ball on the bottom shelf. Color it red.
>
> Put a box on top of the bookcase. Color it green.
>
> Put a car on the top shelf of the bookcase. Color it blue.

Chalkboard (page 116—this drawing can be used many times.)
Activity 1:
> With a blue crayon, write your name at the top of the chalkboard.
>
> With a black crayon, draw a big circle in the middle of the chalkboard.
>
> With a red crayon, make a happy face in the circle.
>
> Color the eraser green.

Activity 2:
> Put a blue circle in the top left-hand corner.
>
> Put a red square in the bottom right-hand corner.
>
> Draw a straight line from the circle to the square.
>
> Put an orange triangle in the top right-hand corner.
>
> Put a green rectangle in the bottom left-hand corner.
>
> Draw a straight line from the triangle to the rectangle.
>
> Put a purple star in the middle of the X.

Name _____

House

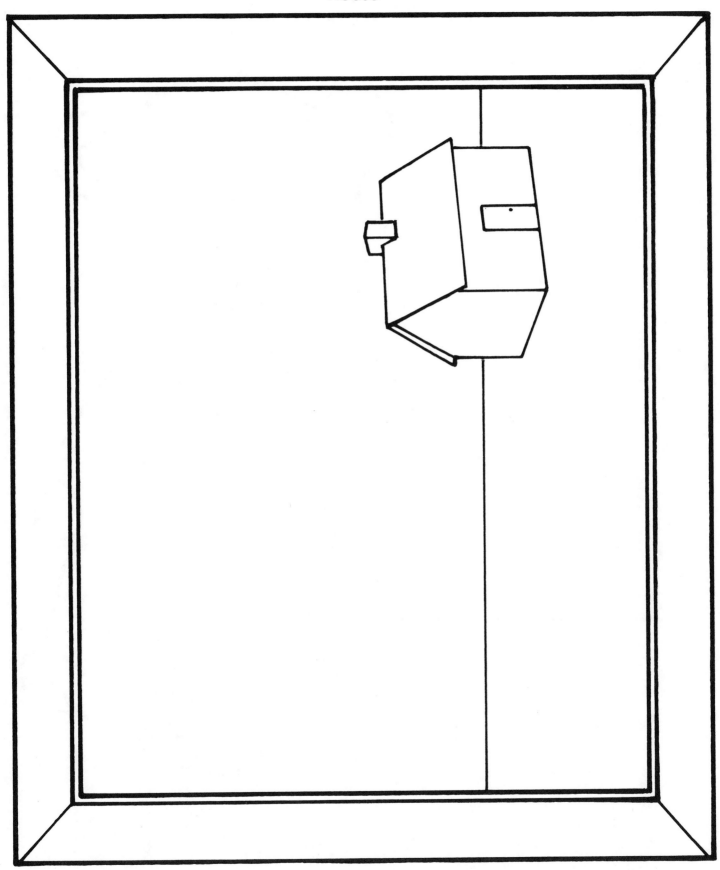

Name _____

Teddy Bear

Name _____

Bookcase

Name _____

Chalkboard

Following Directions

Read these directions to the class one at a time or in multiples, depending on the level of the group. For a different lesson, change or expand the directions.

COMPLETE THE PICTURE 1 (page 118)

Put five apples on the tree.
Put three apples on the ground.
Draw a boy under the tree.

Color the top box blue.
Color the bottom box purple.
Color the middle box yellow.

Put two wheels on the van.
Color the wheels black.
Color the van blue.

Put an antenna on the robot's head.
Give the robot red eyes.
Color the robot's arms black.

Color the stem green.
Color the petals yellow.
Draw two leaves on the stem.

Color the clown's nose red.
Put dots on his bow tie.
Draw a hat on the clown's head.

COMPLETE THE PICTURE 2 (page 119)

Color the balloon red.
Draw another balloon.
Color it purple.

Color the ribbon green.
Put orange flowers on the hat.
Color the hat yellow.

Draw a fishbowl around the fish.
Color the fish orange.
Color the water blue.

Give the dog a bone.
Color the dog brown.
Put a green collar on the dog.

Put two more candles on the birthday cake.
Color the candles blue.
Color the cake yellow.

Put three big red dots on the dress.
Put three small blue dots on the dress.
Color the collar blue.

Name _____

Complete the Picture 1

Name _____

Complete the Picture 2

Crayon-Resist Goldfish Bowl

Materials
    tagboard
    white construction paper
    black waterproof marker
    crayons
    blue watercolor paint
    paint brush
    container of water

Make tagboard patterns for fish and bowl. Trace bowl onto white construction paper, using black waterproof marker.

Have the children:
    Use a pencil or crayon to trace two goldfish into the bowl. Color the fish very heavily with crayon. Cover the entire surface of the fishbowl with blue watercolor paint. (The paint will be absorbed by the uncolored paper and resisted by the wax crayons.)

    Cut out the fishbowl when the paint is dry.

Name _____

Goldfish Bowl

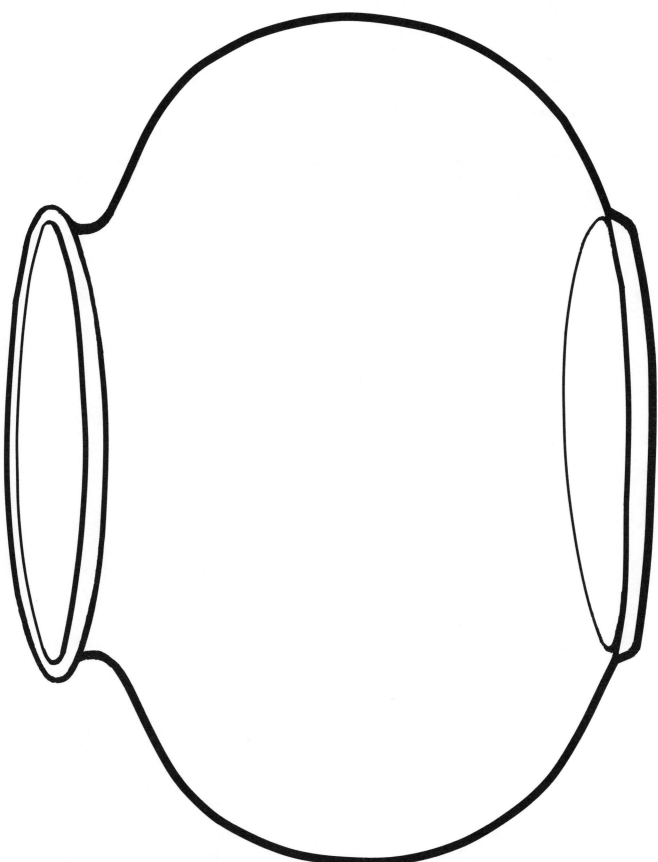

Torn-Paper Snowman

Materials
tagboard
9″ x 12″ white construction paper
6″ x 9″ black construction paper
small piece of red construction paper for the scarf
white glue

Make pattern pieces out of tagboard.

Have the children:
Trace the pattern pieces onto the appropriate paper. Tear around the pieces. (No scissors are allowed.) Assemble and glue the pieces onto a background paper, following the model.

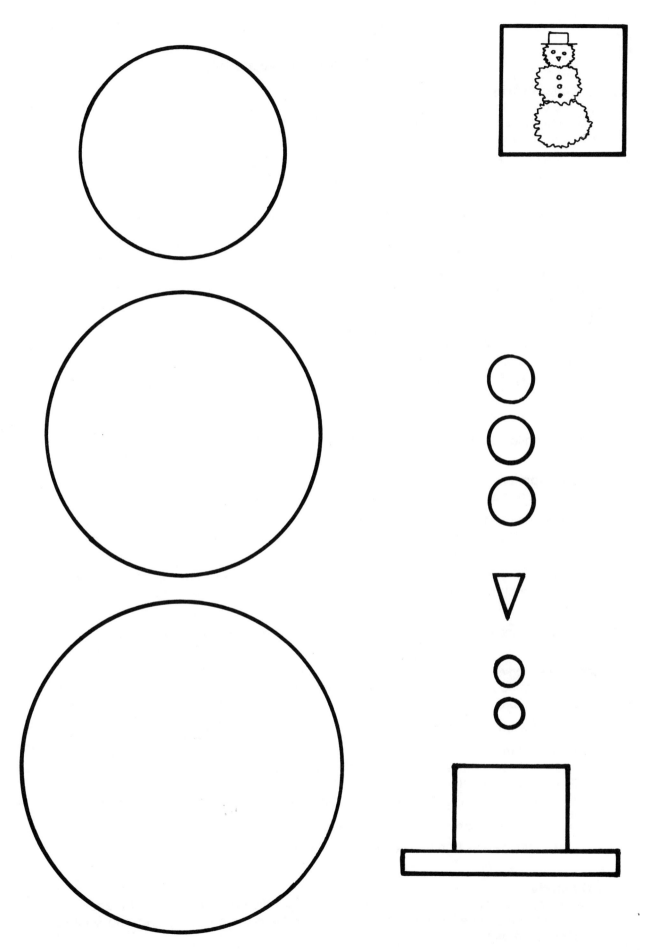

Story Activity

The Billy Goats Gruff Activities

Listening Activity

Tell the children that they are going to hear a story about three billy goats named Gruff. Ask them to listen carefully and not interrupt, so they will be able to answer questions after the story.

Read the story, using the next page for illustrations. Use the sheet as is, color it, or make cards of its parts. Or, read from a favorite illustrated storybook or show a filmstrip of the story.

Ask questions about the events that happened in the story. Include the WH words (who, what, when, where, and why).

Billy Goats Gruff Story Parts

Give each child a copy of the next page. Have them color the parts accurately.

Have different children illustrate story parts, to show:
>   the first billy goat going over the bridge.
>   the second billy goat going over the bridge.
>   the third billy goat going over the bridge.
>   what happened to the troll.
>   the end of the story.

Be sure the details are accurate.

Have the children share their parts of the story with the class.

Finger Puppets

Give each child a copy of the next page. Have them color the parts accurately.

Instruct each child to cut out the bridge and the water and to mount them on a piece of construction paper. The flat part of the bridge goes at the top of the paper. Fold back the paper below the water and stand it upright on a table or desk.

Have each child cut out the troll and the three billy goats. Have them make finger puppets by gluing small bands of paper (to go around one or two fingers) to the back of the puppets.

Encourage each child to use these pieces to tell the story at school and at home.

Sequence Activity

Give each child a copy of the sequence pictures (page 127) and a sheet of 12″ x 18″ construction paper, folded into fourths.

Review the events of the story.

Have the children:
>   number each frame according to the sequence of events (1, 2, 3,4), then color the pictures accurately and realistically.
>   cut out and glue the story pictures in correct sequence on the prefolded paper.
>   each tell the story, using complete sentences.
>   take their papers home to share with their families.

Art Activity

Give each child copies of the pictures of the three billy goats and the troll (pages 128-131). Have the children color and cut them out. Help them make paper-bag puppets (described on page 3).

"Let's Pretend"
Use an opaque projector to enlarge the Story Parts bridge. Trace it onto tagboard and cut it out. Have the children help color or paint it. Covered with clear adhesive plastic for durability, the bridge can be used repeatedly.

Review the story and have the children act out the story using the puppets. Let the children take turns with different roles.

Send the puppets home for the children to act out the story with family members.

Story Parts

Story: The Billy Goats Gruff

Once upon a time there were three billy goats by the name of Gruff. They were Big Billy Goat Gruff, Middle-Size Billy Goat Gruff and Little Billy Goat Gruff. They lived in a valley beside a wide river. There was little grass to eat on their side of the river, and all three of the billy goats were very hungry. They looked across the river and saw up on a hillside a very fine meadow with lots and lots of grass. In order to get to that meadow, however, they had to cross a bridge. Under that bridge lived a mean and ugly troll.

Well, Little Billy Goat Gruff was so hungry he just had to cross the bridge.

"Trip! Trap! Trip! Trap!" went the bridge.

"WHO'S THAT WALKING ON MY BRIDGE?" roared the troll.

"It is only I, Little Bill Goat Gruff," said the billy goat, in a very tiny voice. "I am going to the meadow to eat some grass and get fat."

"Oh no, you're not," said the troll. "I'm coming up there to gobble you up. Here I come."

"Please don't take me, Mr. Troll. I'm very little. Wait for the second billy goat. He is much bigger than I."

"Okay, then be off with you," said the troll.

A little bit later, Middle-Sized Billy Goat Gruff decided to go across the bridge.

"TRIP! TRAP! TRIP! TRAP! TRIP! TRAP!" went the bridge.

"WHO'S THAT WALKING ON MY BRIDGE?" roared the troll.

"It is only I, Middle-Size Billy Goat Gruff," said the billy goat in a voice that was not so small. "I am going to the meadow to eat some grass and get fat."

"Oh no, you're not," said the troll. "I'm coming up there to gobble you up. Here I come."

"Please don't take me, Mr. Troll. I'm not very big. Wait for the third billy goat. He is much much bigger than I."

"Okay, then be off with you," said the troll.

A little bit later, Big Billy Goat Gruff decided to go across the bridge.

"TRIP! TRAP! TRIP! TRAP! TRIP! TRAP! TRIP! TRAP!" went the bridge.

"WHO'S THAT WALKING ON MY BRIDGE?" roared the troll.

"It is I, Big Billy Goat Gruff," said the billy goat in a voice as big as the troll's. "I am going to the meadow to eat some grass."

"Oh no, you're not," said the troll. "I'm coming up there to gobble you up. Here I come."

"Come along if you must, but let me warn you. I have two long horns and four hard hooves."

As soon as the mean ugly troll climbed up on the bridge, Big Billy Goat Gruff butted him with his horns and trampled him with his hooves and threw him into the river. And that was the end of the troll.

The Big Billy Goat Gruff joined the other billy goats eating grass in the meadow on the side of the hill.

And from that day on, the Billy Goats Gruff could always go to the meadow to eat grass and get fat.

Name _____

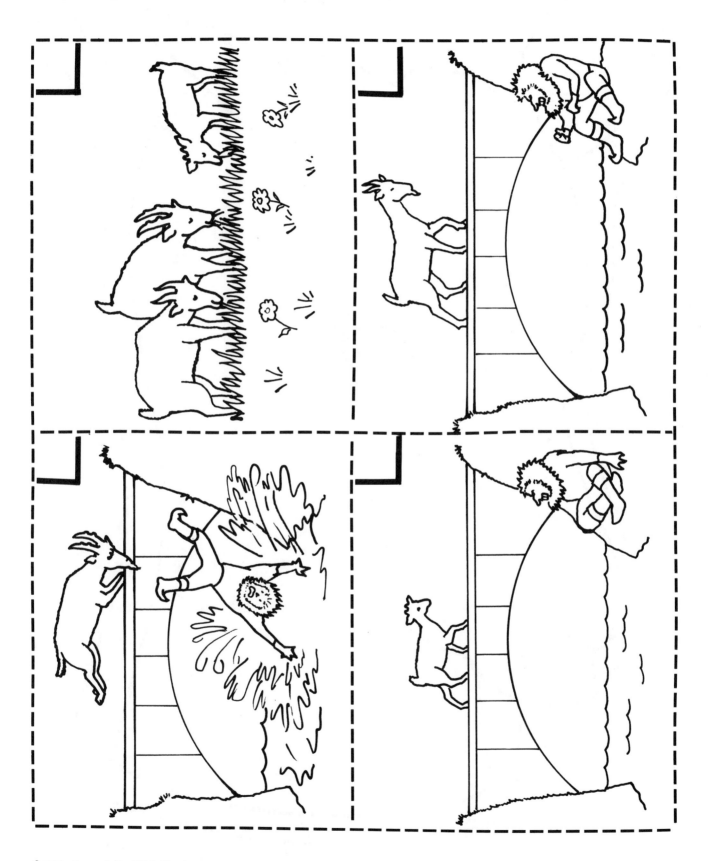

Also by these authors . . .

ALL ABOUT ME: Activities for Learning Language (1986)
Help younger children develop pragmatic language skills and improve self-image with this collection of reproducible activities. These worksheets provide children with opportunities to learn and use basic language skills in developing self-awareness. You'll have worksheets for these topics—colors, shapes, concepts, senses, feelings, self-expression, body parts, clothing, and sequencing.
Catalog No. 7290-Y $16.95

Additional materials to use with your young clients . . .

WORKING WITH CHILDREN'S LANGUAGE (1987)
by Jackie Cooke and Diana Williams
This handbook links theory to intervention strategies and offers ways you can implement these strategies in therapy. You'll have current theory, guidelines for remediation, and activities for early language skills, attention control and listening skills, role of play, development of comprehension, acquisition of expressive language, and perception. For ages birth to 10.   **Catalog No. 7382-Y $18.95**

TELL ME A STORY (1986)   *by Carla S. Kleber*
Meet speech and language goals with these high-interest, low-vocabulary stories featuring full-color manipulatives. Each of the 24 interactive stories presents a storyline of interest to elementary-age students. Stories also include a list of all speech and language targets, colorful manipulatives of the main characters and objects, questions for discussion, dialogue for playacting, and related language activities.
Catalog No. 7303-Y $29

CONCEPTS TAKE SHAPE: Listen-and-Do Activities for Mastering
Abstract Concepts (1986)   *by Mary Jo Anderson and Arlene S. Hayes*
You can provide experiences to teach concepts and strengthen language skills. These programmed activities go beyond paper-and-pencil tasks. Children must demonstrate understanding of concepts by manipulating plastic blocks and laces. These manipulative experiences allow children to interact with their environment. Includes colorful plastic blocks, activity boards, and threading laces.
Catalog No. 2087-Y $24.95

ORDER FORM

Ship to: _____

☐ Please check here if this is a permanent address change.
Please note previous zip code_____
Telephone (_____) _____ ☐ work ☐ home

Payment options:
☐ My personal check is enclosed. Please add 10% for shipping and handling.
☐ My school / clinic / hospital purchase order is enclosed.
   P. O. #_____
   Please add 10% for shipping and handling.
☐ Charge to my credit card. Please add 10% for shipping and handling.
   ☐ Visa ☐ MasterCard ☐ American Express

Card No. _____
Expiration Date: Month _____ Year _____
Signature _____

Qty.	Cat. #	Title	Amount
		Add 10% for shipping and handling. **Arizona residents add sales tax.**	
		TOTAL	

MONEY BACK GUARANTEE After purchasing, you'll have 90 days of risk-free evaluation. If you're not completely satisfied, return your order within 90 days for a full refund of the purchase price. NO QUESTIONS ASKED!
Thank you for your order!
Send your order form to:

Communication Skill Builders

3830 E. Bellevue / P.O. Box 42050 –Y
Tucson, Arizona 85733